Browning
World's Greatest Gunmaker

Browning

World's Greatest Gunmaker

by Gertrude Hecker Winders
with sketches by the author

The John Day Company New York

Published by The John Day Company, 62 West 45th Street, New York 36, N. Y., and on the same day in Canada by Longmans, Green & Company, Toronto.

Library of Congress Catalogue Card Number: 61-8286

Manufactured in the United States of America

To Garry,
my invaluable adviser on guns

Acknowledgments

The author is grateful to many for their help in her research. Especially does she thank Mr. John V. Browning, Vice-President of the Browning Arms Company and grandson of the inventor, for his patience in answering questions and his gracious generosity in making available to her pertinent material never before used.

Among others who have been helpful are: Mr. John James, Jr., Librarian, Utah State Historical Society, Salt Lake City, Utah; Mr. Harmon Williams, Vice-President, Browning Arms Company, Ogden, Utah; Mr. Lee Kay, Chief, Public Relations, Utah Department of Fish and Game, Salt Lake City, Utah; Mr. Orson M. Slack, Manager, Ogden Division, Utah Power and Light Company, Ogden, Utah; Mr. S. M. Alvis, Manager, Ilion Research Division, Remington Arms Company, Ilion, N. Y.; Mr. Thomas W. Bentley, Public Relations Manager, Winchester Western Division, Olin Mathieson Chemical Corporation, New Haven, Conn.; Mr. Edwin C. Shafer, Director of Public Relations, Union Pacific Railroad, Omaha, Nebraska; Miss Caroline Dunn, Librarian, Indiana Historical Society Library, Indianapolis, Ind.; Mr. Charles C. Brockman, sportsman, Indianapolis, Indiana; Mr. C. E. Stinning, Public Relations, Indiana

Bell Telephone Company, Indianapolis, Ind.; Mr. C. William Harrison, author and authority on western lore, Loma Linda, California; Mr. J. W. Hollcraft, retired, Chief Dispatcher, New York Central Railroad, Indianapolis, Indiana; Mr. Henry Stenger, gun authority, Curator of State Museum, Indianapolis, Indiana.

Contents

Browning

World's Greatest Gunmaker

I

In the Shadow of a Gunshop

Snow swept down from the Wasatch Mountains and swirled over the little settlement of Ogden, Utah, that cold day, January 21, 1855. It spread a thick blanket on the flat roofs of the adobe huts. These were the houses the settlers had built of big bricks molded of mud and dried in the sun. Against the rough board walls of Jonathan Browning's gunshop the snow piled in great drifts and sifted through the cracks. Jonathan Browning had built his shop of green fir timber hauled by oxen from the canyon.

Two men entering the gunshop stamped snow from their boots. One pulled off his heavy mittens and blew on his fingers. His breath formed a white cloud. Pale light from smoldering coals in the forge flickered on the guns and tools hanging on the opposite wall. There was no one at work at the bench behind the counter that ran almost the length of the small room.

"Jonathan," Ellis Green called. "Why, where is Jonathan?"

"He must have stepped over to the house," said the other man, Lorin Farr. Farr was mayor of Ogden and also the miller. He put a small sack, half filled, on the counter.

"Let's go see," Green said.

The Brownings' adobe house stood only a few yards away in a corner of their acre of ground. The men walked along a path that had been shoveled through the snow. On both sides of them snow was shoulder high.

At their knock, the door of the house was flung open by tall Jonathan Browning. His eyes twinkled under heavy brows. Though his chin was shaven smooth and he had no mustache, he wore a short fringe of brown beard that went from ear to ear. Now his grin did too—almost. "It's a boy," he announced. "Come in. Come in. My son, John Moses Browning, was born this morning!"

"Congratulations, Jonathan," Ellis Green exclaimed.

"A son. That's fine," Mayor Farr said.

They stepped into a narrow room. A fireplace was at one end. A buffalo robe hung in a doorway at the back.

"You must see him!" Jonathan Browning pulled aside the buffalo robe and disappeared into the room behind it.

"The baby chose a cold birthday," Green said. He walked to the fireplace and rubbed his hands over a feeble flame.

"This weather's no worse than the winters we had in Vermont when I was a boy," Farr said, "but there's no telling how long it will last. I'm glad to see Jonathan saving of fuel."

Mr. Browning came back carrying the baby wrapped in a worn, brown blanket. "He's not fat but isn't he long?" he said, loosening the blanket. "And John's such a strong baby," he added proudly.

"Is he to be John, not Jonathan?" Mayor Farr asked, smiling down at the baby's red face.

"Elizabeth wanted to name him for me. I want him to have a name of his own. Since I am often called Jon, he is John spelled J-o-h-n and we are both satisfied. His middle name is Moses after his Uncle Mose."

"His hand is shaped like yours," the mayor said, touching the baby's pink fist with one finger.

"He'll be helping you in the gunshop before you know it," said Green.

Jonathan Browning chuckled. "Born in the shadow of a gunshop he ought to be a gunsmith," he said. "Now I'll take little John back to his mother and we'll go over to the shop. I have your gun ready for you, Mayor."

In the gunshop a few minutes later, Mr. Browning took down a gun from the rack on the wall. "Here you are, Mayor. Your gun is good as new. I made a new hammer spring."

The mayor nodded toward the sack on the counter as he pulled back the hammer of his gun with his finger. Then he slid the gun to the floor and stood with both hands clasped on the barrel. "I brought you payment from the mill. I figure with another mouth to feed you'll be glad of some wheat flour."

"Wheat flour!" Mr. Browning exclaimed. "Elizabeth will appreciate that. I wish everybody could pay me as well."

"I can't pay you anything now," Green said, "but if I bring my gun will you fix my trigger spring?"

"Of course," Mr. Browning said heartily.

"I haven't forgotten the money I borrowed from you either," Green went on. "I'll pay you as soon as I can, but last season the sun burned up all my crops that the grasshoppers didn't eat."

"It's been a bad year for all of us," the mayor said. "My gristmill, as you know, hasn't been busy at all. But now that the whole seven miles of the big canal from the Weber River is finished we're sure to have better crops next year."

"And now that we're using both adobe and logs on the fort, its walls are good and solid," Green said. "The Indians will be afraid to attack."

"If the grasshoppers'll let us alone," Jonathan Browning said, "we'll be all right. The grasshoppers are worse than the Indians." He frowned. "Usually I don't worry but now that I have little John Mose—"

"He's a fine, healthy baby," interrupted Green.

"A mighty strong little fellow," agreed the mayor.

It was fortunate that little John was a strong, healthy baby or he would never have lived through the hardships the settlement of Ogden endured the first year of his life. In the spring after he was born, tender shoots of corn, peas and beans appeared, only to be killed by frost. A second planting was doing well when clouds of grasshoppers descended on the fields and gardens. Every leaf, every blade of grass, every shoot, every tender twig, was devoured by grasshoppers. There was nothing left for people or animals to eat. The settlers would have starved if they had not eaten roots of weeds.

The next winter brought the heaviest snows anybody had ever seen. Cattle, horses and sheep either starved or froze to death. Snow was so deep nobody could get firewood. The settlers had to use their fences for fuel to keep warm. People from the East, hungry and footsore, pushing handcarts of their possessions, arrived to add to the worries of the settlement. The travelers told sad stories of comrades frozen in the snows of Wyoming.

But little John Moses Browning, snug in his pinewood cradle by the fireplace in the gunshop, blinked happily at the strangers who came to admire him. He didn't know that Indians were fighting in the Cedar Valley not far away. He didn't hear his father mutter at his work, "We may have to use these guns for protection." Little John knew nothing of bitter cold or scorching sun, of grasshoppers or ruined crops. When there was no milk, his mother fed him stew made of thistle roots and he smiled and smacked his lips. He chewed the bulbs of the wild sego lily, and thrived.

Wild Sego Lily, Utah State Flower

II

Indians and the Pony Express

In the gunshop, five-year-old Johnny sat on a stool beside the workbench. His bright blue eyes followed every move of his father's hand as Mr. Browning examined an old gun.

"See the rust, John Mose," Mr. Browning said, rubbing his hand over the barrel. "The owner of this gun didn't keep it oiled. Of course it is an old musket but a gun will last a long, long time if you keep it properly oiled."

Johnny's dog Zip thumped his tail on the floor as though he understood.

"Johnny's learning his trade already, I see," said a man pushing open the door. He swung a gun from his broad shoulder and put it on the counter.

"Yes, John Mose has played in the shop since he was a baby." Mr. Browning pointed to the scrap heap in the corner. "Metal scraps are his toys. He has spent hours digging through the scraps. 'What's this, Pappy?' he wants to know. Yes, he's learning the trade."

"Do you know what a musket is, child?" asked the man, smiling.

"A musket shoots a ball," Johnny said. "That's why it is smaller inside than a shotgun."

The customer's eyes twinkled. "You'll have a gunsmith here before you know it, Jonathan."

"Oh, John Mose understands rifling already," his father said. "Tell why this is a rifle, John Mose," he added, pointing to a long gun hanging on the wall.

"There are grooves cut on the inside of the barrel that go around like this," Johnny said. He moved his small finger in a spiral. "That is rifling. When the ball goes through, it twists like this." Again he made the spiral motion.

"And so," his father said, "it goes truer and farther."

"And so," Johnny repeated seriously, "it goes truer and farther."

The customer burst into a roar of laughter. Johnny wondered what was funny.

"You need a new trigger spring, I see," Johnny's father said, looking at the man's gun.

"How soon can I get it, Jonathan?"

"Right away, Parley."

"Good. I've taken a job with the Overland Pony Express."

"Oh," gasped Johnny, his eyes wide.

"Why, Parley Jones, I'm surprised," Mr. Browning said.

All summer Johnny had heard men in the shop talk about the little ponies running fast, carrying mail across the plains and mountains.

"Will you ride a pony across the desert?" he asked breathlessly.

Again the big man's laughter boomed. "I can't be a rider. I'm about a hundred pounds too heavy for that. The riders are young chaps no bigger than jockeys who ride race horses. You should see them in their red shirts, blue pants and buckskin jackets. I'm going to have charge of a station in the desert."

"You'll need your gun," Mr. Browning said.

Parley nodded. "I know it. Indians have destroyed the stations for fifty miles along the Egan trail."

"How close are the stations?"

"From Sacramento, California, to Carson City, Nevada, they are twelve to fifteen miles apart. Beyond that they are not so close."

"You are taking a dangerous job. I heard that a band of Utes attacked the station at Fish Springs last week."

"I heard that they were Shoshones. They killed the keeper and took his scalp, then stole the ponies he had there."

"Did the Indians have good guns?" Johnny asked eagerly.

"These had bows and arrows, but the Indians can shoot arrows fast as lightning and ride like the wind. Yesterday a pony carrying the mail came into Camp Ruby with an arrow in its flank."

"Will you be scared?" Johnny asked.

"Maybe, but ever since last April when the first pony came pounding into Salt Lake City with the mail I've wanted to be part of the Pony Express. Think of it. Mail from California gets to Salt Lake City in three days. I'll be proud to swing the mochila over a pony and—"

"What's a mochila?" Johnny asked.

"The mochila's a leather cover that goes over the saddle and hangs down the pony's sides," Parley Jones explained. "It has pockets for the mail with padlocks on them."

Mr. Browning bent a thin piece of metal in a vise. "It's wonderful. The Pony Express carries a letter from California to St. Joseph, Missouri, in ten days."

"And the Express is just as fast coming west from St. Joseph," said Parley Jones.

His trigger spring was soon finished and he shouldered his gun. "I'm mighty glad to have this fixed," he said. "My station has portholes to shoot through in case of attack. It is big enough to bring the ponies inside too." He shook his head. "The Indians are getting meaner every day."

Mr. Browning went on working on the musket. Johnny sat thinking about the Pony Express. He knew the little ponies went like a streak. The rider would dismount at a station where the station keeper had a fresh pony ready. He would throw the mailbags—no, the mochila—on the fresh pony and the rider would dash on. It would be fun to ride in the Overland Pony Express.

Zip gave a low growl. The little dog was standing up and facing the door. He bristled and showed his teeth.

Johnny turned around. He felt his scalp bristle.

Three Indians stalked into the shop. Johnny leaped to his feet. His heart beat fast. Zip growled again. The Indians stood still. One was an old man wrapped in a blanket. The others were thin young braves, naked from the waist up. They wore buckskin trousers. Johnny noticed that they had no guns or bows and arrows. All the same he felt a shiver of fear up the back of his neck.

His father half turned to the gun rack. He looked

steadily at the Indians. "Welcome, friends," he said.

The old Indian flung back his head, opened his mouth and pointed down his throat.

"He means he's hungry," Mr. Browning said. "Go, John Mose, and ask Mother to give you some pone and meat."

Johnny ran to the house and told his mother about the Indians.

Mrs. Browning put big chunks of elk meat in a basket. Johnny noticed that her hands trembled.

His year-old brother Matt toddled over and flung his arms around Johnny.

"Matt, you must stay with Mother," she said. She dumped a big pan of cold corn pone on top of the elk meat and snatched up Matt. "Give this to Father, Johnny. And don't go close to those dirty Indians," she added.

His heart thumping, Johnny ran back with the basket. His father took it from him at the door but Johnny darted into the shop. Though he was a little afraid he wanted to see the Indians again.

"Stay back, John," his father said.

Johnny stood as tall as he could by the workbench and watched the Indians grab the food from the basket as his father held it out. Were these mean Indians? They had cross, ugly faces. He wondered if they were Utes or Shoshones. And could they ride like the wind? Or shoot arrows as fast as lightning? Or did they have guns?

The Indians crammed food into their mouths with both hands.

They gobble like Zip, Johnny thought.

When the food was gone, the old Indian thrust out his hand toward Johnny. "How old?" he asked.

Mr. Browning held up his hand with the fingers outspread. "Five," he said.

The old Indian smiled. So did the two young braves.

"Big," grunted the young Indians.

Johnny smiled back. Why, these Indians were not mean. What a nice face the old one had when he smiled.

"White boy, big. Fine brave," said the old Indian.

Then the three stalked out. Johnny ran to the door.

"Wait; don't go outside," his father said sharply.

Johnny saw the Indians swing onto their ponies. They thundered off in a cloud of dust.

"I hope they don't make a habit of this," said Mr. Browning. "That old moccasin-maker comes twice a year to sit under our apple tree and make moccasins and eat your mother's good cooking. I don't want any more Indian visitors."

"But Pappy, I like to see the Indians ride," Johnny said.

"Keep away from Indians," said his father. "Never go any closer to them than you have to. Sometimes they steal white children and take them away to live with their tribe. The Indians near us have been friendly but we can't be sure they'll stay that way." He picked up a long piece of iron. "Want to see how I turn a gun barrel on the lathe? I've been working on this one for a long time."

Johnny perched on his stool again. His father trundled a lathe with his foot. As the lathe turned it shaved off slivers of metal that fell in curls on the floor.

"You can't blame the Indians entirely," Mr. Browning muttered as he stopped the lathe. "Thousands of settlers are moving to the West every year. There're more than forty thousand white people in our territory alone. That means the Indians' hunting land is getting smaller."

Johnny didn't hear him. He forgot the Indians and even the Pony Express as he looked entranced at the new, long, round gun barrel. And to think Pappy had made it from an old, rough, worn-out iron wagon axle!

III

Gunshop or School?

Six-year-old Johnny sat on the floor of the gunshop behind the box he called his workbench and filed a piece of metal. He was all by himself in the shop because his father had gone to Great Salt Lake City on business. His cheeks were streaked with grease. He was sure he looked like a real gunsmith. In the scrap pile he had found a scrap almost the shape of a gun hammer. I can make a hammer out of this that Pappy can use in a gun, he thought happily.

He had started to school that week and didn't like it. Although he went to school only in the morning, he was already tired of sitting on a bench with a row of other children. "I'm not going any more," he said to himself. "I'll stay home and work with Pappy in the shop."

He heard a rattle of wheels and a man's shout, "Whoa!" A wagon was pulling up in front.

I'll have to get Mother, he thought, dropping his file. He ran to the house. "Come quick, Mother," he called. "Somebody is coming." He dashed back.

The wagon, he noticed, was loaded with bags of salt. Salt was easily obtained from Salt Lake nearby. Johnny had often seen big iron kettles filled with lake water hung over fires along the shore. The briny water, boiled down, yielded quantities of salt. Sometimes trenches were dug near the lake to catch the water, much saltier than the ocean. After the sun evaporated the water, salt was left in the trenches.

Johnny was behind his little workbench as the customer with a shovel over his shoulder walked in.

"Where's your father, son?" he asked. "I want this shovel mended."

"Pappy's in Great Salt Lake City," he answered.

Mrs. Browning, a little out of breath, hurried into the shop. "My husband is away but he'll be back day after tomorrow," she explained.

"I'll have to leave the shovel then," the man grumbled. "This will delay me. I'm driving through Ogden with a load of salt and I did hope the gunsmith could mend my shovel while I waited."

"I'll make out a repair tag for you," she said.

Johnny watched his mother write the man's name on the tag and tie it on the shovel.

"When will it be done?" the man asked.

"Oh, Wednesday—or perhaps Thursday, I'd better say."

People brought all sorts of things to the gunshop to be mended. She put the shovel in a corner with a pitchfork, two hoes and a broken skillet.

"Don't you need salt? I'd like to pay in salt."

"Very likely you and my husband can arrange a trade," she answered.

After the man left, Mrs. Browning said, "Your father is not going to be pleased with all the repair work I have taken in for him."

"Pappy hates to mend shovels and skillets," Johnny said.

"I know," sighed Mrs. Browning. "Before you were born he had his shop right downtown. He moved here so people wouldn't bother him with little repair jobs but they come anyway." She looked at guns with tags dangling from them to the tools waiting to be mended. "I think it's a good thing. These little jobs pay."

"But Pappy wants to work on his new gun," said Johnny.

He didn't know how to explain it to his mother, but he could understand better than she did how annoying it was to be interrupted when you were making something. Johnny liked to make things too and school interrupted him.

"I forgot to put the date on that tag," Mrs. Browning said. She scribbled numbers on the tag tied to the shovel.

"Mother, show me how to write a repair tag."

"You have to know how to write and how to spell before you can fill out a repair tag," she answered.

"Can't I learn all that?"

"Of course. You can learn it in school."

Looking thoughtful, Johnny rumpled his light hair. Next morning he trotted off willingly to school.

A week later his mother noticed Johnny one night sitting on the floor cutting brown paper into small oblong pieces. "These are my repair tags," he explained. Beside him was a neat pile of tags.

"I can print letters but I can't spell the names yet," he said. "Will you help me with the names?"

"I'll help you," she promised. "Let's start with short ones like Green and Pratt."

Night after night by the kerosene lamp on the table Johnny printed names on his tags. He made tags for everybody he could think of, even those with long, hard names. On his little brother Matt's he printed his full name, Matthew Sandefur Browning. He found his mother's name, Elizabeth Caroline Browning, a hard one to print.

"As soon as I can fill out repair tags by myself," he said, frowning as he carefully printed a *z*, "I'm going to quit school."

"You'll have to learn about the dates on the calendar and how to figure the cost of a job too," she reminded him.

He didn't quit school but the sessions were not long. He had a lot of time to spend in the shop and all the time he was there, playing or working, he was listening and learning.

IV

Arrows and an Indian

But Johnny was an outdoor boy too.

Canals running from the meeting of the Ogden and Weber rivers and a network of ditches brought water to Ogden gardens and farms. They also provided fun for the boys.

In the canal near his home Johnny went fishing with the neighbor boys. He caught suckers, chubs and an occasional trout washed down from the river. His playmates fished with bent pins until they saw the fishhooks Johnny made in the shop. Then he had his first customers. The boys bought his hooks or traded for them.

He was only a little fellow when he learned to swim. Going swimming was simple. On a hot day he would slide out of his shirt and jeans and dive into the canal. The sparkling water was always cool and clear.

One spring day a group of boys came over to the Brownings' back yard to play. Johnny was eight but the others were older.

The air smelled sweet with fruit blossoms. A breeze scattered petals of pink and white from the big apple tree near the barn. Johnny glanced up at the distant mountains. The last of winter's snow still outlined the tops of the mountains in white against a bright blue sky. But the sun was warm on Johnny's blond head.

"Let's play Indian," a boy suggested. His father had fought Indians at Bear River a few months before.

"No, let's go swimming," said another.

There was a chorus of, "The water'll be too cold."

Then a big boy of twelve ran into the yard. He was waving a bow in one hand and a bunch of arrows in the other. "See my new bow and arrow," he shouted.

The boys crowded around him.

"That's a good one, Bill," Johnny said, noting the even curve of the bow.

"Let me shoot it," a boy suggested.

"Me too," said another.

"You can all shoot," Bill said generously. "We'll take turns."

"I'll make a target," Johnny said, "and nail it to the Indian tree."

"What's the Indian tree?" asked a boy who was a newcomer to the neighborhood.

Johnny pointed to the apple tree. "We call it the Indian tree because an old Indian comes here twice a year and sits under the tree making moccasins."

"I think Johnny's too young to shoot," Heber Roberts observed, watching Johnny nail a board to the apple tree. With charcoal, he had drawn a bull's-eye with two rings around it on the board. It annoyed Heber to see a younger boy do so many things that he could not.

Johnny's eyes flashed. He gave the board a final bang with his hammer. "I'm as big as you are, Heber Roberts."

"You're only eight," Heber said. "I'm two and a half years older. You have to be careful with a bow and arrow. My brother was shooting rabbits the other day and shot an arrow right into our cow."

"Did it kill her?" Johnny asked.

"No, it didn't go deep but she was so upset she can't give milk."

"Our cow's way down behind the barn," said

Johnny impatiently. "Nobody's going to shoot that far and I can shoot as well as anybody."

"I'll bet he can too," said the new boy.

"Of course he can," said a boy.

"We all have to be careful," Bill said. "We'll make a rule that everybody must stay behind the shooter. That way if an arrow goes astray it won't hit anybody. Of course Johnny can shoot."

One by one the boys took turns. Most of them shot within the rings. Bill shot the bull's-eye. So did the new boy and Heber.

Johnny was the last to shoot. He felt a shiver of nervousness as Heber handed him the bow. "Next time," said Heber, "only those that hit the bulls-eye ought to shoot."

"All right," Bill agreed. "And each of those will shoot twice."

"Johnny will probably hit the barn," Heber said.

Johnny noticed that Heber's mouth was pulled in the shape of a bow upside down.

The instant Johnny faced the target he forgot everything except that round spot. His bright eyes measured the distance. His hand, big for a boy of eight, nocked the arrow, and twanged the bow. The arrow went straight to the bull's-eye.

"Good," Bill exclaimed. "Now the four of us will each shoot twice."

Johnny waited impatiently as the others shot. Bill's arrows were both way off the mark. The new boy shot in the circles. Heber shot one in the bull's-eye, the other in the outer ring.

"I could hear Mr. Browning pounding his anvil in the shop," Heber explained. "That ruined my shot."

A sudden gust of breeze blew Johnny's light hair in his eyes as he was ready to shoot. He shook back his hair and waited a moment, eyes on the target. Then he shot straight to the bull's-eye. He was smiling as he nocked the next arrow. Since babyhood he had been using his hands to make things. Perhaps that was why his hands closed so confidently around a bow. To shoot straight to a mark didn't seem difficult to Johnny. He had had little experience with a bow and arrow but he was sure he could hit this target again and again.

He shot as the wind bent the treetops, swooped across the yard blowing a blizzard of blossom petals and chicken feathers. It swerved his arrow off the course and carried it high in the air beyond the tree just as a tall Indian came around the corner of the barn.

Horrified, Johnny watched the arrow. It seemed going straight at the Indian.

"You shot him," Heber squealed. "What did I tell you?"

"Good-by," said Bill, snatching his bow from Johnny.

The others ran.

The arrow fluttered harmlessly to the ground in front of the Indian.

Johnny, heart thumping, went forward and picked it up. He pointed to the target on the tree.

The Indian's deep-set eyes glared.

Johnny pointed to the arrow and waved his hand to indicate the wind.

The Indian's fierce expression did not change.

How could he convince the Indian that he was not trying to shoot him? He began again pointing to the target, to the arrow. Then he saw the bundle in the old fellow's lean hand. This Indian was the moccasin-maker! He knew how to deal with him.

Johnny ran to the house. As he opened the door the delicious odor of fresh-baked bread floated out to him. To Johnny it smelled sweeter than apple blossoms.

"Mother, the moccasin-maker is here," he called.

But there was no one in the house. No doubt his mother was taking care of the shop. Johnny's father was often called away suddenly to be consulted on some church or community business, for he was a much beloved and respected man.

This was no time to ask permission. Six big loaves

were cooling on the table. Usually fresh wheat bread was too much of a treat to give to an Indian but this was an emergency. Johnny grabbed the biggest loaf.

The Indian was already sitting with his back against the apple tree. His arms were folded on his chest. His tools were beside him. Spread before him on the grass was a piece of beautiful, soft buckskin.

Johnny held out the loaf. The Indian took it and bit off a sample bite. He chewed it solemnly. Johnny supposed he had never tasted wheat bread before. Was it possible that he didn't like it? He watched anxiously as the Indian took another bite. Then he took another and another. When half the loaf was gone he said "Ugh." Since this was all he ever said, Johnny took a deep breath of relief.

He gathered up the arrows Bill had left behind him. That afternoon he gave them to Bill. "That's a good bow and arrow, Bill," he said, "but I'd rather shoot a gun."

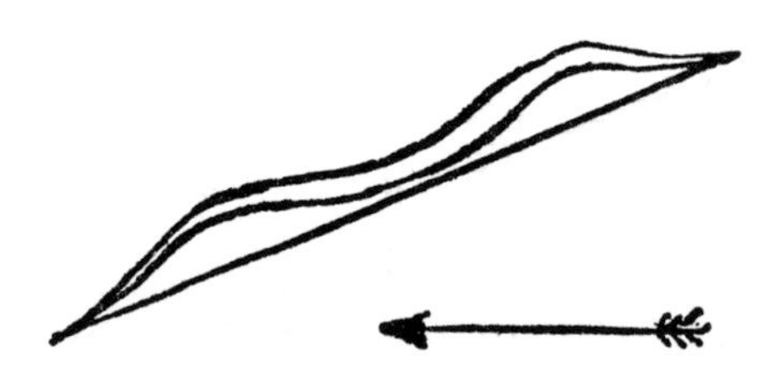

V

Hunting with a Gun

With his father, Johnny was going hunting one bright October morning. He was now eight years and nine months old, tall for his age and strong, strong enough to carry a long rifle over his arm ready for action.

Usually his father went out late in the afternoon to get birds for breakfast and Johnny would go along to carry the game. He always fired a shot or two from Pappy's gun, too. Today was different. They were going in the morning and he was carrying a gun. It was a real hunt.

Though the sun made the aspen groves on the mountainside shine like pure gold, the air was sharp. Johnny was glad he was wearing his buckskin jacket. The tops of the rugged mountains were white with the first snow of the season. The sky was clear, cold blue.

Like his father, Johnny stepped lightly through the canyon bordered with aspens. Their branches looked white as snow among the quivering golden leaves, he thought. Above them stretched the dark green of pines. Here and there a dwarf maple or chokecherry tree glowed like a flame.

Johnny did not tell his father but his eyes were alert for any tuft of feathers sticking up behind a bush. "Stay close to the settlement," his mother had warned them when they left. "It's said that the Indians are on the warpath again."

"Not likely in northern Utah after Colonel Connor's battle with the Shoshones at Bear River last January," his father said. "That was nearly sixty miles from here but I think it has put an end to any Indian trouble throughout the whole territory."

They had left the neat squares of gardens and cultivated fields behind them. Johnny looked quickly from side to side as the trail led them through a thick forest of pines. The trees grew straight up over a hundred feet. What good poles for tepees could be cut here, he thought uneasily. A branch quivered. He caught his breath, then laughed. A flying squirrel sailed through the air ten feet from one bough to another. His keen ear heard the snap of a twig, and his heart came into his mouth. A deer darted across the trail.

He was glad when they reached a level open space of dried grass. Here no Indians could hide. It would be a good place for wild chickens, too. Grasshoppers rose in a cloud as they stepped through the grass.

There was a flash of wings overhead. In one quick motion he brought his gun to his shoulder and looked up. Three sea gulls were flying low.

"They look like pigeons," Johnny said, watching the graceful birds dip and circle. "Why does nobody ever shoot sea gulls?"

"Their meat wouldn't be fit to eat," said his father. "They're scavengers. They'll feed on anything as the buzzards do. Then don't you know the story of the gulls?"

"Oh yes, I did but I've forgotten."

"Never forget the story of the gulls," his father said. "In Great Salt Lake City the settlers had sowed crops early that year and they were doing well. It was in 1847 before I came out here. Then in early June there was a terrible frost followed by crickets, millions of them. They blackened the earth. They ate everything. All the pioneers could do was pray. Then the sea gulls flew in from an island in Salt Lake."

"And gobbled up all the crickets," Johnny added.

"That's right," his father said. "The gulls were an answer to prayer. It was a miracle. If the gulls had not come I doubt if the settlement could have lasted a year. Grasshoppers are bad this year but—" He broke off. "Look, over there."

Johnny saw a flock of wild chickens feeding.

"You shoot first, Johnny."

Johnny's heart thumped, but his hands were steady. He cocked his gun, pulled it to his shoulder, and shot. He felt the jar of the gun against his shoulder.

Bang! The shot was loud in the cold air. Immediately came the crack of his father's rifle. Mr. Browning was using a new single-shot rifle he had just finished making.

"We both got a bird!" Johnny shouted. He ran ahead to pick up the two chickens.

When they came home at noon Johnny proudly carried a bag of four wild chickens and five ruffed grouse.

"I've hunted in Kentucky, Illinois and Iowa, but Deseret is the best of all," his father said. "Big game, little game—we have everything in Deseret territory."

"You like the name Deseret better than Utah, don't you?" Johnny remarked.

"Of course, that's the name the settlers gave it, and Deseret means honeybee. I like that, for we should all be as busy as bees. But somebody in Washington, without consulting us, decided to name the territory after the Ute Indians, and certainly we have no reason to like the Utes."

The face of the smiling old Indian who had called him a "fine brave" so long ago flashed into Johnny's mind. He thought, The Utes were here first.

"I have worried about you," his mother greeted them.

"Why?" Johnny asked.

"The Indians know about the war among white men in the East," she answered. "That will stir them up again."

"Perhaps it will," said his father. "This War Between the States is a terrible thing. Brothers are fighting brothers. I'm glad we are a long way from it."

"Yes, in spite of the Indians, I'm glad we are out here," his mother agreed.

"Oh, I wouldn't want to be any place else," Johnny said. He was thinking of the snow on the mountains, the gold of the aspens, the scarlet bushes like fire among the evergreens, the smell of pine, the exciting flash of a deer, the flutter of wild chicken wings, and especially the crack of a rifle in the clear, cold air.

VI

The Wagon Train

"Matt, don't touch the gun," Johnny said. "It may be loaded. I haven't had a chance to check it." He was busily filing rust off a barrel.

Matt pushed closer to study the beautiful gun on the counter. Its stock was elaborately carved with birds and flowers.

"The fellow who brought it in says that the gun is a Colt, made back East in the factory where they stamp out the parts by machinery," Johnny added. "But this is a special gun made for a gift. The stock is all handwork. Be careful," he cautioned again.

"There," Matt said, putting his hands behind him, "does that suit you? I'm not a baby. Next year I can shoot."

"Next year we'll go hunting together," Johnny

agreed, "but you have to learn to be careful with guns. I'm careful. So is Pappy. So is everybody who knows anything about them."

He was now eleven and knew so much about guns that for a year he had often been left alone in charge of the shop as he was today. He could weld, drill, use the lathe, make new parts and put a gun together. Once he had even made a gun of an old flintlock barrel, a board, some wire and a scrap of tin. It had no trigger or hammer but he had fired it with a lighted stick and killed three prairie chickens. However, it was a crude affair hastily made. He was ashamed of it and tore it up.

Johnny liked work in the shop but he hated chores. By trading fishhooks, and bows and arrows which he made, in exchange for work, he induced his friends to do some of the milking, digging in the garden and wood chopping that he was supposed to do.

"Have you done your chores?" he asked Matt while he whirred the file back and forth.

"I filled the woodbox. It's your turn to bring in water," said Matt firmly. "I'm going to sit here in the doorway and count things."

It was a warm August afternoon. As Matt sat on the doorstep clouds of dust swirled in the street. The top of the cottonwood tree that shaded the gunshop shook with the rattling sound of leaves drying in the sun. The air smelled of dust and cottonwood leaves.

Matt liked to count. "I see one rooster and one-two-three hens scratching in the street," he chanted. "I see one, two men riding to town." He looked in the other direction and jumped to his feet. "One, two, three, four, five—oh, Johnny, come see all the wagons. Such a lot. There're more around the corner. And they're coming this way!"

"Surely not the whole train." Johnny came to the door. "I wonder if they're freighters or people moving out West."

The drivers of freight wagons were called freighters. The freight wagons carrying supplies to be sold were often called freighters too.

The same men who had managed the Pony Express were in the freighting business. They sent big prairie schooners loaded with tons of goods across the western trails. The Pony Express had made its last run when the overland telegraph system was finished in the fall of 1861, five years before.

"That's long train," Johnny said, looking at the oxen-drawn covered wagons approaching, "and I suppose they'll stop here. You go get Pappy. He's over at the Roberts'. They're having trouble with their ditches and he's showing them how to fix them."

The boys waved. As long as he could remember, Johnny had been waving to wagon trains, though not often from his own front door. The shop was on the edge of town out of the stream of traffic. The rush to California to gain a fortune in gold had started the year before Johnny was born and ever since, wagons had been rolling over the plains, into the Salt Lake valley and up to Ogden. It was a favorite place to rest and buy supplies. Immigrants, hunters, miners, passed through the town. Some would turn west to California; some go north to the beautiful, wild mountain region that was to become Idaho and Montana.

"They'll be here soon," Matt said, jumping up and down.

"Yes, and they'll want a million things done at once. Now go get Pappy right away."

Matt, looking back from time to time at the wagons, ran down the street.

The wagons pulled up. Men, women and children tumbled out. The men crowded into the shop.

"Where's the gunsmith?" they shouted. "Where's the gunsmith?"

"I'm the gunsmith," Johnny said calmly.

"That child can't work on my gun," said one man. "When will your father be here?"

Another handed his gun to Johnny, but he looked worried.

"Your mainspring's broken," Johnny said. "You left a load in when the spring broke, didn't you?"

"That's right," said the man.

Johnny quickly whittled a stick and put it in the nipple so that no spark could reach the powder when he worked on the gun.

The owner of the gun stared. "Boy, you certainly know how to handle a gun."

Now a dozen men came to the counter with their guns.

The shop buzzed with loud voices. The travelers wanted to know about water holes on the trail west and were the Indians hostile? And didn't Browning have any new guns for sale? They had heard back in Iowa that he made repeating rifles.

Johnny was glad to see his father's tall figure in the doorway.

"As fast as I can make a gun it's sold right here," Jonathan Browning explained.

A big man, sunburned dark as an Indian, thrust out his hand. "I'm captain of the train, Mr. Browning."

"I know what a job you have," said Mr. Browning as they shook hands. "I was captain of a wagon train myself from Council Bluffs, Iowa, to Ogden in 1851."

Matt ducked under the elbows of the crowd. With him was a boy about fourteen years old. "Johnny, here's a fellow that has fought Indians and shot bears," he said. "His name is Joe."

"We had five Indian attacks on the plains," said Joe. "I was in the thick of every fight." He patted a bowie knife at his belt. "If it hadn't been for this I'd have lost my scalp. An Indian grabbed me by the hair and I cut his tomahawk right in two."

Johnny saw that Matt's eyes were getting wider and wider. "Tell about the bears," Matt said.

"Oh, I shot two man-eating grizzlies as we came into Ogden. And did you ever see a mountain lion?"

"I shoot one every morning before breakfast," Johnny said. He winked at Matt. "We eat them—raw."

After one startled look, Joe laughed as hard as Matt did. "Maybe I was telling tall tales," he admitted, "but we did have one skirmish with Indians not far from Omaha and it was not funny."

"We want to see your repeaters," the captain's voice rang out. "I saw one you made in Kanesville, Iowa. It was a mighty fine gun."

"Johnny, you show them the repeaters while I get to work," said his father.

The color in Johnny's cheeks deepened a little as he took down the old slide repeater his father had made in Iowa years before. He had never shown the repeaters. His father always did that.

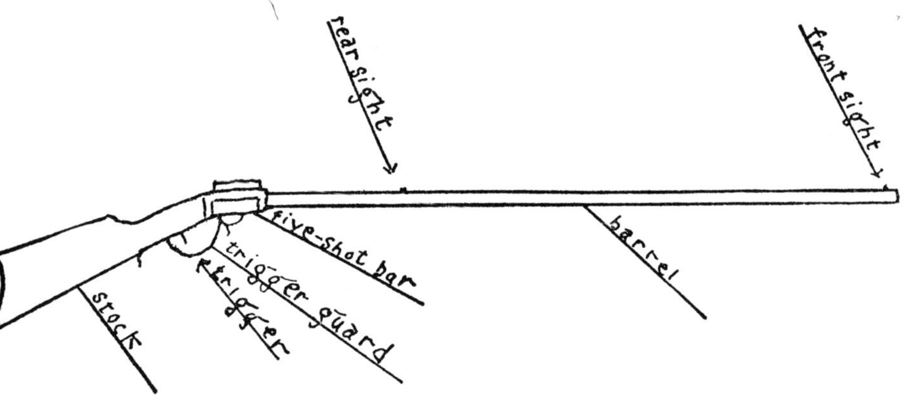

John's Father's "Slide" Repeating Rifle

"Here, on the outside of the gun, is this bar of iron with five holes in it," he began.

"Wait a minute," a man exclaimed. "I can't see it."

Johnny waited until the man, a short fellow, had squeezed in front of some tall ones.

He went on, "A load goes into each hole. When you want to shoot, you slide the bar with your hand, this way." He slid the bar into an opening in the breech. "When the load is in the right place, fire. You can slide the bar five times. That gives you five fast shots."

"Pretty good," said one.

"That's handy," said another.

"Would be simple to make," said another.

"It's not so fast," Johnny said, "as this other that Pappy made later." He turned to the other rifle. "It's a six-shooter. The ball and powder are loaded into the six slots in this cylinder. When you draw back the hammer, the gun is cocked and the cylinder revolves."

"That's a copy of a Colt," the captain said. "Here!" He pulled his revolver from its holster. "This is my Colt. I wouldn't start west without it. See. When the gun is cocked, the cylinder revolves, bringing the load in line with the barrel. He's copied a Colt."

"My father designed this himself," Johnny said indignantly.

Jonathan Browning left his work and came to stand by his son. "I learned gunsmithing when I was a boy where the best guns in the world were made—the mountains of Kentucky," he said sternly. "At that time nobody had ever heard of Colt. I designed and forged my first repeater in 1831 before Colt ever started. Don't talk to me about copying Colt."

"I—I'm sorry," the captain said, "but the principle is the same."

"Through the mountains you'll find many a good gunsmith making guns on this principle, I expect," said Mr. Browning. "Any reason why not?"

"The Colt revolver is patented and—"

"My gun isn't," Mr. Browning said. "A gun is mighty important out here on the frontier. Every man must have one. All I ask is a fair price for the best gun I can make and I make it myself, in my own way, every step by hand."

Matt was in front of the crowd. His chin rested on the counter. He looked at his father with sparkling eyes.

"You make good guns all right, Mr. Browning. You're the best gunsmith we've met on our whole trip," the captain said.

Two days later the boys waved good-by to the wagon train. The last of the riders on horses trotting beside the slow-moving wagons were past. In the last wagon Joe leaned out to wave to them.

"Johnny, what is patented?" Matt asked.

"Oh, if you have an invention you make a design of it and send it to the patent office in Washington, D.C. The office keeps your design with your name on it with a number so nobody else in the whole country can make one like it."

"But you can make all you want?"

"Of course, it is your own invention."

"Samuel Colt patented his revolver," Matt said. "One of the men in the wagon train came from Hartford, Connecticut. He says that Colt lived in a house like a palace. He was a very rich man when he died."

Johnny answered proudly, "They said Pappy was the best gunsmith they ever met."

VII

Making Moccasins

"Mother," said John one morning, carrying in an armload of kindling he had just chopped, "our Indian is here."

"Which one?" she asked. "There's an Indian boy about fifteen who's been coming to the door begging lately. He calls on your Uncle Mose, too."

"This is our old Indian, the moccasin-maker," John answered. "He's already at work under the Indian tree. What shall I take him for breakfast?"

"Here are some biscuits, and venison. Take him plenty or we won't have many apples left on that tree."

He had been taking food to the moccasin-maker a good many years, John reflected as he walked down the path with a bowl of good things to eat. It was four years since he had almost shot the Indian with his arrow.

The Indian had spread a piece of buckskin on the grass. His lean hand guiding a sharp knife cut into the leather neatly. Holding the bowl, John waited. He knew from experience how annoying it was to be interrupted when you were working on a job that required skill. Never before had he noticed how carefully the man worked. He's a real craftsman, he thought.

Finally the Indian lifted his knife, looked up. John put the bowl down. In a twinkling the Indian had eaten everything in the bowl. Then he picked up a big needle from the few tools laid on a dirty rag beside him. As swiftly as John could have cocked a gun he threaded a thong through the needle.

John crouched down and watched. There're tricks to making moccasins, he thought. I never realized it. The sun rose higher. John forgot the buckets of water he was supposed to carry to the house and shop. Occasionally a ripe apple plopped from the tree above him. John didn't hear it. He was fascinated by the moccasin-maker, intent on every move of his deft, quick hands.

At noon he coaxed Matt into helping in his place in the shop. Matt was only eight but he was handy with tools.

John went back to watching the Indian. He watched a second day too, all day long. Neither said a word, but John brought out especially good meals and the Indian's grunts were more satisfied than usual. No doubt he appreciated the tribute to his skill.

On the third day he was gone.

"If I had some buckskin I could make us some moccasins, Matt," John said. "I know how."

"Shall we go hunting?" suggested Matt.

"No. It takes too long to tan a skin. Anyway, only Indians know how to do it right. They pound it and work it and I don't know what else they do to it, but they have beautiful buckskin. I want to get a skin from an Indian, and I have a plan."

His blue eyes danced with mischief as he outlined his plan to Matt.

Next day when the Indian boy who came often to beg strolled from the Brownings' back door munching a chunk of pone, John popped out of the shop. He was armed with a new bow and arrows which he had made. With a bow and arrow he was now so expert that he could hit a rabbit or target any time. Now, pretending to shoot carelessly, he shot at a target on the front of the shop.

The Indian stopped, watching John intently. John paid no attention to him.

The wood of the target was soft. The arrows

went in deep. Slowly John pulled them out. He knew that the Indian was watching every move and admiring those sharp arrows. John stepped back and nocked an arrow.

The Indian sprang forward. He grunted and pointed to the bow. His black eyes gleamed. He thumped his chest and motioned toward the bow again. Plainly he wanted it.

John held the bow toward the boy and then withdrew it.

This was the signal for Matt to do his part. He ran into the shop and came back with a ragged scrap of buckskin. His father had cut patches for bullets from it.

With an arrow John traced on the ground an outline of the piece of buckskin he wanted. Then he went through the motions of stretching the scrap of buckskin to cover the space he had drawn.

The Indian nodded. He understood that John wanted a big piece of buckskin. Then with motions John promised him the bow if he brought the buckskin.

The boy narrowed his eyes. John could see that he was asking himself, "What trick is this? Would the white boy really give me the bow?"

John handed him an arrow. The Indian clutched it but he looked at John suspiciously. John thrust the whole bundle of arrows into his hands. The boy grabbed the arrows and ran away.

"Now you've done it," said Matt. "Wasted all those good arrows."

"He'll be back," John said. "What'll he do with the arrows without a good bow?"

In three days the Indian boy brought John a fine piece of buckskin and John gave him the bow.

One afternoon a few days later John and Matt walked uptown to the band concert in beautiful, new, buckskin moccasins.

"John made them," Matt told everybody who exclaimed over them.

On every side John heard, "They are beautiful. Make me some, John."

A man stopped him. "John, my wife says you repaired her sewing machine the other day. You're like your father; can do anything. I'll be glad to pay you a good price if you'll make me a pair of moccasins like yours."

But John refused. "I won't make any more moccasins," he said. "I don't want to be a cobbler. I'm a gunsmith!"

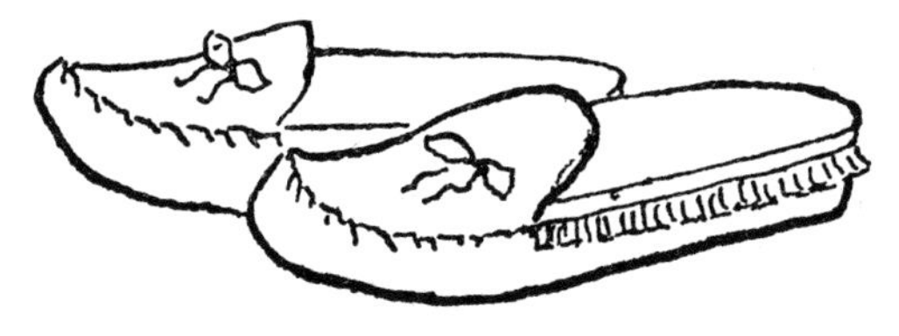

VIII

Two Good Guns

One day, working with his father, John noticed a heavily loaded freight wagon drawn up at the door. The freighter came in carrying a badly mashed shotgun.

"Can you mend it? I know it's in bad shape. A heavy box on the wagon fell on it," the freighter explained.

Mr. Browning examined the gun carefully. It was possible that it could be rebuilt, he said, but it would take a month of work before it could even be tested, and then he couldn't guarantee the result. New parts would have to be made. It would be a big job. The gun was really not worth it.

The freighter nodded. "I'm sure you're right,

but what shall I do? I have to have a gun. What have you for sale?"

Mr. Browning had on hand a good rebuilt gun. Without hesitation the freighter slapped a ten-dollar gold piece on the counter in payment, a good price. "Here," he said, thrusting his broken gun into John's hands, "want a gun, sonny?" He picked up his new gun and swaggered out.

John turned the ruined gun in his hands and felt a mounting thrill of excitement. He was thirteen and had never had a good gun of his own. This gun had been a little beauty. He rubbed the barrel. Most of it was good. The action was beyond repair. But he could make parts, couldn't he? He began to whistle softly as he reached for a screw driver.

He worked on the gun in his spare time for two months. The result was a good, lightweight shotgun that was the pride of his heart.

Matt was as delighted with the gun as John was. At breakfast, enjoying the wild chicken John had brought home from his first hunt with the new gun, Matt was thoughtful. If John could build a gun out of the freighter's smashed shotgun, why couldn't he build one out of the material in the shop? Why can't he make me one? Matt wondered.

He passed John the hot biscuits and pointed out an especially choice piece of chicken. "Mother, can't we open some chokecherry jelly?"

Jelly made from the wild chokecherries was John's favorite, Matt knew. He would wait until John was well filled with chicken, biscuits, jelly and gravy before asking him about the gun.

After breakfast he followed John out to the shop. John went to work immediately.

Matt leaned his elbows on the counter and kicked at the scraps and filings on the floor. A gun was a big thing to ask for. He didn't know what to say. His feet touched something that rolled. Braced by his elbows he hopped up on it and rolled back and forth while he wondered how to begin. Finally he said, "Uh—John—how—when—I mean how soon—"

"How soon what?" asked John.

"How soon are you going to make me a gun?" Matt blurted out.

"As soon as you find me a barrel that's fit to use," John answered.

Matt's feet slipped from under him. He sat down on the floor hard. He came up waving the thing he'd been rolling on. "Here!" he yelled. "John, here's a barrel."

John burst into laughter. "How did you do it?

If you aren't the smart one. Pappy hasn't made a barrel in ages and the tools are scattered. You knew what I'd say."

Matt held an old barrel covered with grime and filings. It was one Mr. Browning had tucked under the bench years ago and forgotten. Matt had some difficulty convincing John that it just happened to roll out at the right time.

John was already scraping at the thick coat of dirt. "I could have sworn I knew every screw in the place but I never saw this," he remarked, squinting into the hole in the barrel. "We have a box of old parts for slide rifles that Pappy brought from Council Bluffs. I can use some of those."

"Then you're going to make me a rifle?" Matt asked breathlessly. He had thought of a shotgun but now the rifle seemed exactly what he most wanted.

John looked straight at Matt. His blue eyes were stern. "If I make you a gun you'll have to carry in the water and chop the wood all the time I'm working on it," he said. "And it'll take a long time."

"You always figure a way to get out of chores," remarked Matt.

"I do. I hate a clumsy spade or shovel or ax. I prefer small, neat tools."

"All right. Use your small, neat tools on my gun

and I'll take care of the wood chopping and bringing in the water."

"And I'll have to persuade Pappy to let me take time to make the gun. You know I have a lot of work to do in the shop. Pappy will be here soon so go get a bucket of water now. A fresh, cold drink will put him in a good humor. And get chopping, Matt. Mother complains that she never has enough firewood now that I'm so busy in the shop."

Matt sighed but trotted off to bring a bucket of water.

Pappy was easily persuaded and gave him a beautiful piece of walnut for the stock. It took John four months of his spare time to make Matt's gun. In October, on Matt's ninth birthday, he presented it.

"Oh, it's a beautiful rifle," Matt gasped. "A really good gun."

"It's time you had a good gun," John told him. "You already shoot better than most men."

The brothers tramped miles through forests and canyons. They kept the family supplied with deer and small game. They lay in the marshes near Salt Lake waiting happily for the noisy clatter of thousands of ducks rising in the air. Together they hunted bear and antelope in the mountains.

Matt liked to hunt for fun and thrills. So did John. But since he had made the two guns, he found himself puzzling over a problem every time he fired a shot. Was the action as smooth as he could make it? he asked himself. Could he build a gun that would shoot faster?

Early in his teens he began to dream of a new, a better gun. He began to whittle in wood an idea for a rifle that would be sure, swift, smooth in operation and different from any gun that had ever been made.

The school day in Ogden was short. Busy though he was with repair work, he took time to whittle his dream in wood and to try to build it in metal. He worked on it long hours. No more bow and arrow making. No more moccasins. Dreaming and building the ideal gun became an absorbing interest that was to stay with him always.

IX

The First Train

One March day in 1869, John and Matt were coming home from a hunting trip in the Wasatch Mountains. A deer John had shot was lashed by the legs to a pole which they carried on their shoulders. On a ledge of the mountainside they stopped to rest.

Behind them rose the mountains broken by canyons. Tall pines were dark against patches of snow. Below lay Ogden, rows of houses made into neat squares by streets and irrigation ditches. Beyond the town westward, open country stretched to Great Salt Lake.

A pair of bluebirds darted through the leafless aspens near them.

"Salt Lake today is as blue as the bluebirds'

wings," Matt said, turning his head to watch the birds' flight. Then, "Look, John!" he exclaimed, pointing to the south. "How close to town the tracks are."

Like giant crayon streaks the iron tracks of the Union Pacific Railroad crossed the wild landscape.

"All that good metal in tracks, when I have to save every scrap in the shop," John remarked. "Miles of rails! And they weigh fifty to fifty-six pounds a yard. Wish I had some of that iron to work with."

"How fast they're working," Matt said.

"Maybe the two railroads will meet right here in Ogden," John answered.

Matt grinned. "Wouldn't that be fun?"

The Union Pacific, building west from Omaha, Nebraska, and the Central Pacific, building east of Sacramento, California, were running a frantic race. The United States Government had agreed to pay each railroad a bonus of money and land according to the amount of track it laid before they met.

In silence the two boys watched the swarms of men at work laying the tracks. Then they picked up their deer and went on down the rough trail.

Two days later Matt, dressed in his Sunday clothes, rushed into the shop.

"Come on, John," he urged. "Come right away or

we'll be late for the parade. I've been waiting for you."

The great day had arrived. Not that the tracks had met in Ogden, but the Union Pacific tracks had reached there. A train, the first the citizens of Ogden had ever seen, was going to steam into town.

Chinese workmen, hired by the Central Pacific in California, after tunneling through mountains were reported struggling in the desert west of Ogden. Of course, the Irishmen who laid the track for the Union Pacific had had their troubles with mountains and sand too.

John, in his best clothes, slowly rubbed an oil rag over a gun barrel. "Oh, we'll get there," he told Matt.

"If you and Pappy don't putter around the shop forever," Matt retorted.

"We have work to do. Why didn't you go with the others if you're in such a hurry?"

Their mother had already left for the celebration. So had their younger brothers Sam and Ed.

"Come on," Matt answered, running to the door. "I can hear the band."

With Matt and his father, John walked toward the tracks. Once started, he could share Matt's excitement. The roll of the drums seemed to carry him along. The blare of the brass horns made his blood run faster. The tune ended in a thrilling clash of sound. The crowd burst into applause.

Lorin Farr, still mayor of Ogden, climbed stiffly to an overturned box. "Fellow citizens," he shouted, "this is the beginning of a great era. What seemed impossible ten short years ago has been accomplished!"

What does he mean by saying *ten short* years? thought John. That's a long time. Why, I was only a baby four years old ten years ago and Matt was just being born.

"The West will soon be linked with the East by railroad," Mayor Farr said.

"Hurrah," yelled the crowd.

Mayor Farr held up his hand for silence. "This is only the beginning," he said. "Ogden is going to become a great railroad center!"

In the distance John saw a black spot that grew rapidly larger. Puffs of smoke floated over it.

"The train!" he exclaimed.

"The train!" others shouted.

Some one pulled at John's hand. "Where's the train, John?" His little brother Ed looked up at him. John boosted him onto his back.

"It's coming! The train!" rose in a mighty cry from hundreds of voices.

Far down the track the train whistled in answer.

John's heart beat fast. What must it be like to go whizzing across the country at forty to fifty miles an hour?

Now it was closer. It looked like a monster, a fire-eating dragon in a child's story. The whistle shrilled loud.

The chug of the engine vibrated through him. He heard the clash of wheels, smelled smoke, had a moment almost of fear as there came a rush, a blur, as the iron monster passed.

Belching smoke from the wood-burning engine, creaking and squealing, the train slowed, stopped. The Union Pacific Railroad had come to Ogden.

How the crowd cheered.

The engineer yanked a steam valve. The iron monster gave a terrific hiss. John's ears buzzed. Then a blast from the whistle seemed loud enough to shake the mountains. The engineer leaned from his cab. "Now I'm going to turn the train around," he shouted.

The shriek from the crowd rivaled the train's whistle. In terror most of the crowd scattered and ran like excited chickens.

Of course, the Browning boys didn't run. Little Ed began to cry. "Don't be afraid, Eddy," John told him. "The train can run only on the track."

Men and women as well as children were running wildly to escape. There was a big slough near and some plunged into it. In places they waded knee-deep in mud.

"Come back," Mayor Farr shouted above the clamor. "There's no danger."

"Oh, where is my little Isaac?" a mother wailed.

"Susan," another cried. "I have lost Susan."

The band began to play a rousing march.

"Come," the mayor called. "We'll parade through town."

Men, red-faced, struggled out of the slough. Women and children were helped to dry land.

The band led the way downtown with many following, but John and Matt stayed behind to help find terrified children who were still hiding. It was nightfall before John found little Isaac shivering under a serviceberry bush.

On the eleventh of May, about two months later, John and Matt were eagerly reading a newspaper spread on the counter of the shop. The day before, the two railroads had met at Promontory forty miles northwest of Ogden. Two newspapermen from Salt Lake City had brought a printing press to Ogden and issued a newspaper about the event. A golden spike had been driven to mark the final meeting of the rails.

Several men were in the shop talking about the Golden Spike ceremony.

"It says here that Governor Leland Stanford of California struck the first blow on the golden spike with a silver hammer," said John.

"I can tell you something that the paper probably missed," chuckled a man. "There was a telegraph wire fastened to the silver hammer. The governor's blow was to be heard at a certain time across the country as a signal to start celebrations all along the line. Well, Governor Stanford swung down with the hammer and missed the spike by about a mile."

"You don't mean it!" Mr. Browning exclaimed.

"I didn't know that," said Mayor Farr.

"It's a fact," the man said, laughing. "There would have been no signal to flash across the country at the expected moment if a quick-thinking telegraph operator hadn't made a click to start the celebrations."

While they laughed, Matt asked, "Did they really take a photograph? And will the picture show the two engines at Promontory and all the people just the way they really looked?"

To Matt, a photograph seemed as wonderful as the railroad.

"What a time of change this is," his father said.

"First we had the Pony Express, then the telegraph, and now railroads and photographs. And how our town is growing!"

"Our population in 1860 was 1,463," said Mayor Farr. "I expect double that by next year. With so many new people we must expect more changes around Ogden."

"Hunting around Ogden doesn't change," John said, glancing up from the newspaper. He thought of deer, elk, bears and bighorn sheep, of wild ducks, grouse and sage hens. He looked out of the open door. Patches of bright green shone on the mountainside in the May sunshine. He knew just how the air would feel on the trail this morning—bracing and fresh. A house finch was trilling its song in the cottonwood tree. "At least I hope it never does," he added, picking up the wooden model of a gun he had been working on for a long time.

Whistling softly he began to whittle. Men will always want to hunt, he thought. They will always need good guns.

X

The First Patent

John grew into a tall, lanky young man. He had a pleasant, humorous mouth, keen, rather deep-set blue eyes and a shock of sandy hair, darker than it used to be. He moved with the easy grace of the outdoorsman. His hands were skillful and steady, and so swift that when he swung a gun to his shoulder and pulled a trigger, his hand and the trigger were one blur.

He knew more about guns than anybody in Ogden, but he never contradicted customers if they tried to tell him exactly how a gun should be made. He just grinned to himself and went on working in his own way. Ideas for improving guns whirled in his lively mind. In experiments he learned much about hardening and tempering steel by heat. He worked steadily to develop his designs in steel.

John was nineteen when he finished his first gun according to his own design. He slipped off alone to test it in the field, and came back to the shop smiling.

"It works all right, Pappy," he announced.

"I knew it would," his father answered. "I'm proud of you, John Mose. That's as good a gun as I ever made, and I doubt if there's another gunsmith in the territory who can make its equal."

John's heart sang. "I want to make another," he said, "only a little different. But it takes so much time and the repair jobs mount up."

"You work on gunmaking all you want to and leave the repair work to the other boys," Mr. Browning said.

By this time three younger brothers, Ed, Sam and George, in addition to Matt, were learning gunsmithing. Will was the only boy in the family who was not interested in guns. He became a printer.

So John, whistling softly, worked on, experimenting, trundling the old lathe his father had hauled by oxen from Council Bluffs, drilling, chiseling, filing by hand. Matt pronounced the next gun John made perfect.

"But Matt, I have another idea," John said.

Matt saw a faraway look in John's blue eyes as

though he was intent on something Matt could not see.

"If I make a lever that opens the breech," John went on, "it can eject the cartridge case, cock the gun and drop the hammer down almost out of sight, out of the way for aiming." He sketched a few lines on paper. "Like this."

Matt studied the paper. "If you can do that," Matt said thoughtfully, "you'll have a design to patent."

John nodded. "That's what I'm figuring on."

He went on eagerly with his work.

Mr. Browning was growing old. Also he had interests besides the gunshop. More and more the responsibility of the shop was left to John. In 1878, when John was twenty-three, his father gave him the gunshop. "You've earned it ten times over, John Mose," he said. "You manage it in your own way and maybe you and the boys can make more out of it."

"I'll try, Pappy," John promised.

He was thinking more seriously than usual about making money, for he was planning to marry pretty Rachel Child.

On May 12, in 1879, the same year that he married Rachel, he applied for a patent on his single-shot rifle. The patent was granted to him that fall on October 7. It was the first of one hundred and twenty-eight patents that were to be issued to the gunmaker, John M. Browning, in the course of his long career.

XI

Six Hundred Guns

In the late fall of 1879 John and Matt faced each other sadly in the old gunshop. Jonathan Browning had died the week before.

"We ought to build a better building," Matt said. "Pappy always meant to have one."

"I know," John said, "but he didn't have the money for it and neither do we." His eyes were on the bench where his father had worked so many years. "It seems only yesterday that I was a little tyke sitting on a three-legged stool watching Father turn a gun barrel or take a gun apart. How we shall miss him. Pappy was a genius."

"There's no doubt he was the best gunsmith in the territory, but you're better, John."

"What nonsense," John exclaimed. Indignation sharpened his usually pleasant voice. "I know what

I'm doing, but when I think of Pappy designing and forging a repeating rifle with the crude tools he had in Iowa. Why, he probably had never seen a repeater. He was wonderful."

Matt nodded. "But you're better, John. Pappy always said so. You're clever with your hands the way he was and you think ahead farther and quicker than he did. I'm glad your patent papers came before he died. He looked them over again and again. He was so proud of you! I can hear him now, 'John Mose has plenty of inventive imagination.' "

John flushed. "He always encouraged me. If I can be as good a gunsmith as my father I'll be satisfied."

"I won't," Matt said. "John, this patent is only the beginning. We can have a big business. What did Pappy accomplish building his fine guns one by one?"

"He made them on order. He sold everything he made."

"And nobody has ever heard of Jonathan Browning except a few mountain men," Matt went on. "But look at Colt. He patented his revolver and made guns by the thousands in his factory. He died a rich man and his armory is going right ahead today. Colts are world-famous."

John thrust his hand through his tousled, longish

hair and smiled. "My single-shot rifle is patented. Thinking of making Brownings world-famous?"

"Of course not, but we can make them pay better than Browning guns ever have."

"How, when we sell all we can make?"

"Let's start in a big way. Imagine the racks on that wall behind you filled with new Brownings—say two hundred guns." Matt swung around and pointed to the opposite wall. "Build racks to cover this wall and put up another three hundred guns. Fill the space over there with racks. What would a customer think if he walked in and saw on display six hundred beautiful, smooth-working Browning guns!"

"Six hundred guns," John repeated looking around at the shabby walls. He was beginning to feel some of Matt's enthusiasm. "They'd look beautiful."

"Then we'd really be in the gun business, in a position to command a fair price," said Matt. "We've been nothing but a little frontier shop and we've been selling at less than our guns are worth. Now we have a patented design for a crack rifle. Nobody can make one like it and—"

"But six hundred guns. How—"

"We can do it," Matt interrupted, "if you'll agree that it's a good idea."

"It's a good idea all right."

Matt clapped his brother on the back. "We'll do it!"

With the help of their brothers, Ed and Sam, they began to build rifles on John's patented design. They decided not to sell any until they had six hundred finished.

"But what do we do," Ed asked, "if somebody wants to buy a gun for a good price when we have a big stock of fifty or so on hand?"

"Fifty!" exclaimed Matt. "Don't call that a big stock."

"Six hundred is our goal," John reminded Ed.

"If somebody wants to buy one simply say that our guns are not yet for sale," said Matt.

"But don't forget we have plenty of fishing tackle for sale," John added.

The boys worked hard but it was tedious work, all done by hand. After a month of using every minute they could spare from the usual selling and repair work in the shop, they had finished only ten rifles.

"It will go faster after the first month," John declared.

"Are you sure it's a good idea to have so many finished without any orders?" Ed asked.

"Matt says so," John answered, "and I bet nobody ever gets ahead of Matt on a business deal. Matt's smart."

They had many chances to sell guns. One day a man came in determined to buy. "Just name your price, John," he insisted.

"I'm sorry," John said. "Our guns are not for sale."

"You boys must be daffy." The man stamped out of the shop.

"The Browning boys have some foolish notion of having a big display of guns," the man's wife told a neighbor. "My husband was ready to pay cash for a gun, and do you know, John had the impudence to say the guns are not for sale."

"I never heard of such a thing," the neighbor said. "Indeed, that's not the way their father did business."

The neighbor told her husband about the Browning boys' peculiar project so he went to the shop to see if it was true. It was, he told a friend afterwards. They shook their heads and agreed that at least John, a grown man and married, ought to have more sense. The friend on a train to San Francisco entertained a crowd with a complete account of how the boys were building a stock of the best guns in the world, rifles made on the John M. Browning patent.

"I'd like to have one of those rifles," said a man.

"So would I," echoed through the car.

"Suppose they're waiting for an Indian uprising to sell the guns at a big price?" asked another man. "The Indians are getting restless again. We're going to need guns."

But the Browning boys had not given a thought to possible Indian uprisings. They simply wanted to have six hundred guns on display at once. They worked hard and they worked long hours. Because his deft fingers were the most skilled and because he was so eager to reach the goal, John worked the hardest.

While the boys worked day after day, week after week, month after month, people went on talking about the Browning boys and their excellent guns. Tongues wagged on the farms, in the mines, in the lumber camps, and on the railroads radiating from Ogden—the Union Pacific, the Central Utah and the Northern Utah.

A year went by, two years. To complete the six hundred guns required almost three years. At last the great day arrived. John stacked three rifles in the one front window of the little shop. Inside, five hundred and ninety-seven guns were arranged in impressive rows.

One of the first men to enter the shop asked, "Which of you boys is the inventor?"

"My brother John," said Matt.

The man shook hands with John. "Congratulations on a good gun. I represent the Winchester Repeating Arms Company. I want to talk business with you."

John's heart leaped. Winchester was an important gun company back East in New Haven, Connecticut. He glanced at Matt. Matt's eyes sparkled but there was no smile on his lips.

"Then you must talk with my brother Matt," John said. "He manages our business."

"Winchester wants to buy your entire stock," the visitor said.

"W-What?" gasped Ed. "I'll run tell George and Sam."

"The whole six hundred guns!" John exclaimed.

"And we also wish to buy the patent to manufacture them."

Matt said, "Whatever your offer we cannot decide hastily, but will be glad to give it our consideration."

XII

The New Shop

The Browning brothers agreed that the offer from the Winchester Repeating Arms Company was satisfactory. They sold all their six hundred guns, and the patent to manufacture them, to Winchester in 1883.

"Hurrah," Matt exclaimed. "Now we have money for a better building."

John and Matt stood under the cottonwood tree in front of the old gunshop. Between the upright boards of the shop the cracks had been filled with strips of unfinished wood. John pulled off a scrap of shriveled bark. "These walls look like the hide of a mangy old buffalo," he remarked.

"I have my eyes on that two-story brick building down the street," Matt said.

"Isn't it pretty big for us?" John asked.

"Not a bit too big," Matt answered. "We'll have a store downstairs and you can have a workshop on the second floor where you won't be disturbed."

They bought the building and erected on the front a large sign decorated with a painting of a gun. BROWNING BROS. appeared in big letters and in smaller letters, J.M. BROWNING AND BRO., GUNS, AMUNITION AND FISHING TACKLE.

John's schoolmaster might object to the spelling "amunition," but nobody else would care. Ogden was delighted with the Brownings' good stock of the popular makes of guns, and experienced sportsmen as the boys were, they could give customers expert advice. Their success was certain, everybody said.

To John, the best part of the new store was the workshop upstairs.

"John, you devote yourself to your inventions. I'll manage the business," Matt offered.

"It doesn't seem fair to shove all that work off on you while I'm puttering around in the workshop," John said. "If business grows as we expect, there may be a lot of bookkeeping."

"I hope so," Matt replied. "I like keeping accounts and haggling over contracts and guessing ahead on how much and what to buy. Besides, your 'puttering around' is mighty important. This sale to

Winchester is a good start." Matt's eyes shone. "We can make money on your ideas, John. Go ahead and putter."

John grinned. "I have no objection to making money but I don't like managing business very much, Matt. You go ahead and manage."

So the arrangement suited both brothers exactly. Each could use his special talents to the best advantage in their business.

John and Matt posed to be photographed in the doorway under the sign of their new shop. For the picture, their brothers George, Sam, Ed and his dog, and a gunsmith they had hired, stood outside. Each man held a gun. Rods and reels hung in one window. Guns were stacked in the other. What a fine-looking sporting goods store! Ogden was proud of the Browning brothers.

"That's the best rifle in the world, John," an enthusiastic customer declared. "It's smooth, accurate and fast. You're a wonder, boy."

John grinned and looked down, feeling his thin cheeks redden. He honestly wished people would not pay him compliments. They embarrassed him. He knew whether a gun was good or not. His new single-shot rifle might even be the best in the world, but out hunting with Matt one day he had decided that it was not fast enough to suit him.

To Matt, hunting meant the joy of being outdoors, the excitement of the chase, the thrill of discovery of new game, the sense of achievement over a well-filled bag, or contentment by the campfire after a hard day in the wilds, but to John it meant all this and something else. Every shot John fired was now an experiment, a scientific test. Eyes, fingers and nerves alert, he pulled the trigger, sure that the bullet would go to its mark, but critical always of the mechanism under his fingers. When he was working on it he had been happy over the new rifle. It was manufactured within two years and was called Winchester Model 1885. Its lever worked smoothly, ejecting the empty cartridge, sinking the hammer almost out of sight.

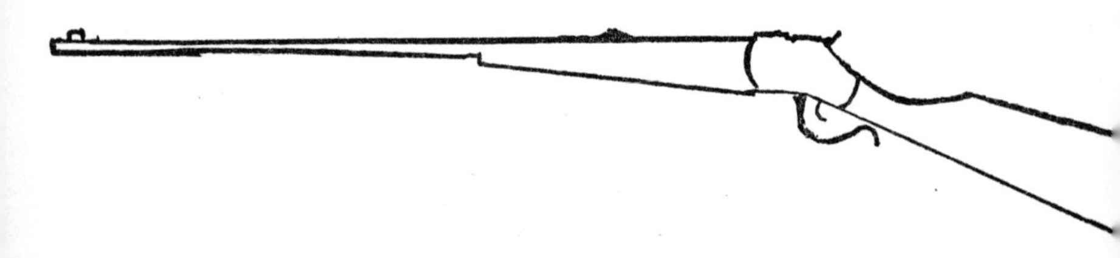

First Invention, Model 1885 Single Shot Rifle

But even before the six hundred guns were built, his lively mind had leaped ahead to a new design. By the time the sale was made to Winchester he was drawing designs for a new type of repeater.

"John," an old man advised him, "you better

quit tinkering, for you can never make a gun to equal your single-shot rifle. Best rifle in the world."

John nodded. A few minutes later he was climbing two steps at a time upstairs to the workroom. Spreading his drawings on the table he began to whistle. Ahead of him were hours, days, weeks, of patient tempering steel, cutting, experimenting, dreaming and working, but right now his heart leaped in time to his whistled tune. He knew the repeating rifle he was designing was going to shoot much faster than "the best rifle in the world."

In October 1884 he obtained a patent for his first repeating rifle. Immediately Winchester bought the patent. Two years later it appeared as Winchester Model 1886.

This model had a lever that could do everything that the lever on the single-shot could do and could reload the gun besides. With lightning swiftness the lever opened the breech, cocked the gun, ejected the empty cartridge, picked up and inserted a new cartridge into the chamber, closed the breech and locked it. In less than a second's time the hunter's trigger finger would be ready for the next shot.

"Fastest gun I ever fired," said the hunters. "Smoothest lever-action job ever developed," said gun authorities. So the praises poured in.

But John was never satisfied with his results. He

made other repeating rifles and sold them to Winchester, but his '86 was the forerunner of all his later lever-action rifles. With modifications, it was to be manufactured for over seventy years.

Yet it did not displace his first invention, the famous Winchester Single-Shot Model '85.

"I want the single-shot '85 for my boy," said a farmer coming to Browning Brothers to buy his son's first gun. "It's cheaper, and I figure that a single-shot is safer in the hands of a beginner than a repeater."

"It's lighter, too," John said.

So the single-shot still sold. So popular did it remain that it was adapted to more calibers than any single-shot or repeating rifle in the world.

Not only Winchester was to manufacture guns under John M. Browning's patent, but other important companies were destined to make Browning-designed guns. Among them were Colt, Remington, Savage and Stevens.

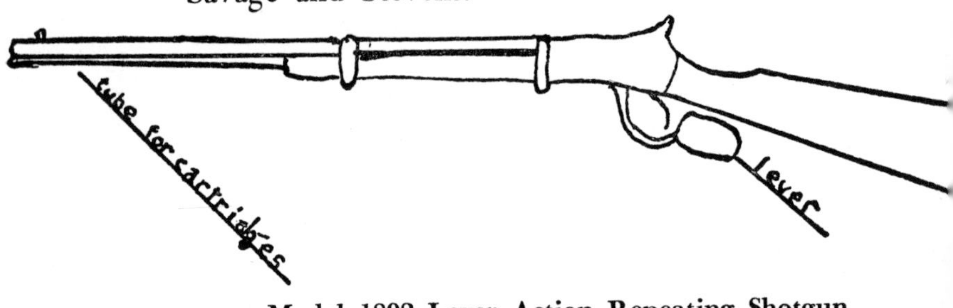

Model 1892 Lever Action Repeating Shotgun

XIII

His First Pump Gun

One morning Matt came into the shop to find John studying a letter from Winchester.

"What's the matter, John? Rifles not selling as they should?"

"No, not that, but Winchester has asked me to make a repeating rifle for them that will take the little .22 caliber short cartridges. You know that will mean a light gun for a repeater and I've been thinking—" His voice trailed off as the faraway look came into his blue eyes. He stared past Matt at the opposite wall.

"You can do it, John. You'll come up with a bright idea."

"I usually do," John admitted, but he added slowly, "but maybe not, this time. It won't be simple. A lever on a light gun may upset the balance.

What if I didn't have a lever?" He turned toward the stairway. "I'll have to put aside my work on autoloading guns and work on this."

Upstairs he began to draw plans, only to stop and whittle on a bar of wood, to file a sliver of steel. Then back to his drawing board. On the floor beside him discarded sketches soon covered scraps of wood and metal. He was still working steadily when the setting sun reddened the windows. He did not look up until lines blurred before him in the twilight. He reached up and turned on the new electric light. It was a single bulb dangling on a cord from the ceiling. The light glowed bright for a few moments. Then it blinked out.

Although service was somewhat better since the Electric Company had remodeled its hydroelectric plant in Ogden Canyon, it was still uncertain. Before the remodeling, many in Ogden thought that the town should abandon electricity in favor of gaslights. Now John lit a kerosene lamp and went on drawing.

"Coming, John?" Matt called upstairs.

"No. Please telephone Rachel and tell her I'll be late." The telephone had come to Ogden eleven years before. "I still have something to work out." Whistling softly, he studied his sketch.

Matt knew that John might work all night.

Gripped by an idea, John lost all sense of time. Once he had worked twenty-four hours straight.

His new design was for an entirely different kind of repeater. Underneath the barrel was a wooden tube that was to be pumped back and forward after each shot. This was called the pump- or trombone-action model.

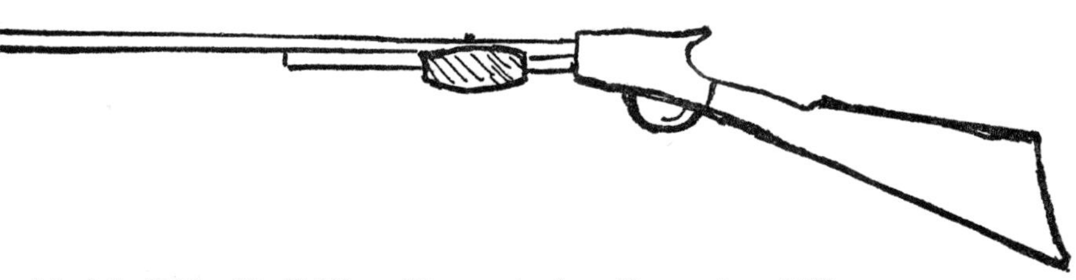

Model 1890 .22 Caliber Pump Action Repeating Rifle, First Trombone Action Model Manufactured by Winchester

They want this as soon as possible, he thought as he finished his design, some days later. I'll mail these drawings right away without making a model.

Winchester replied promptly. He tore open the letter eagerly. As he read it, his jaw dropped in astonishment. "What—what's the matter with them!" he exclaimed. "They tell me to quit working along this line. Matt, listen to this: 'Our experienced company technicians say that the design you propose cannot possibly work.' "

"I'll bet they're wrong," Matt said.

"Of course they're wrong," John said indignantly. "I know that'll be as good a gun as I have ever made."

Matt laughed. "I'll take your judgment over that of an army of company technicians."

"So will Winchester," John muttered. "I'm going to make that model myself."

According to the plans he had submitted, he began to build a working model. This time he did not whistle as he worked. His jaw was set in a grim line. His hands moved surely and swiftly. He liked working with metal better than drawing plans.

The trained technicians back East had the advantage of the finest tools and the best of modern materials. John still used his father's old lathe. His tools were simple and he often built with scrap metal. Old railroad car axles he prized as especially good material. On the outside his model might show some of the crudities of hand construction, but for all that, he was sure he was right!

When his working model was finished he loaded it with .22 short caliber cartridges and confidently fired it at a target. It worked perfectly.

He sent his gun to Winchester with the following message:

You said it wouldn't work but it seems to shoot pretty fair to me.

Winchester did not hesitate.

"They like it," John told the boys jubilantly. "My gun is to be the first pump-action Winchester has ever produced."

"And the first repeater anybody has manufactured that handles the .22 cartridge efficiently," Matt reminded him. "I'm proud of you, brother!"

Split Allen, an old prospector, was in the shop buying ammunition.

"How did you manage that pesky little .22 cartridge, John?" he asked.

"You see I have two steel fingers grip a shell at the rear of the magazine," John explained. "They draw it out while ejecting the old shell and put the fresh one in the right place."

The old man nodded. "You're a smart boy, John."

"Smart," Ed echoed. "Our brother's a genius!"

Sam chuckled. "John has fun making guns," he said, "and we get our fun bragging about him."

"Oh, quit," John said, but he felt a deep glow of happiness. As much as he disliked extravagant praise from strangers he enjoyed his brothers' faith in him.

"When's the new gun coming out?" Split Allen asked.

"Very soon, in 1890," John answered. "It's to be called Model 90 .22 caliber pump-repeater." He brushed a tired hand over his forehead. The .22 caliber pump-repeater had cost him much sleep, work and some worry.

"You're working too hard," Matt said. "Take a vacation. You need a hunting trip."

"Come with me," Split said. "I've pitched camp on a high mountain stream full of trout. Prettiest spot you ever saw. I've got a grubstake to last a long time, and huntin' and fishin' up there is of the best."

"What about gold?" Matt asked with a grin.

Split was supposed to be prospecting for gold, but everyone knew that he did most of his prospecting with gun and fishing rod.

"I don't guarantee anything but plenty of deer and trout," retorted the old man, "and maybe a bear."

"That sounds good to me," John said. He felt exhausted. His eyes looked sunken under his heavy brows. He had lost his healthy outdoor color. "Only I don't know if I can spare the time."

"You go!" his three brothers answered together.

XIV

Grizzly in the Mountains

Next day Split proudly opened a door made of small logs which he had set in the mountainside. "I've tunneled out a cellar here for my meat," he explained.

John stepped into a room or cave about twenty feet deep. Its walls were hung with slabs of bacon, great chunks of smoked bear meat and quarters of venison.

"This will last me a long time and didn't take long to get," said Split. "There's plenty of game up here. You'll see. You may even bag a grizzly."

"That would be a thrill," John said, his heart quickening. He was glad he had come.

That afternoon as they set out hunting, Split led a packhorse to carry the game. John breathed deep of the clear air. His step was light. Already his tiredness was leaving him.

Only a quarter of a mile from camp he shot a deer. While he helped Split dress the deer he leaned his rifle against a tree. The horse became restless when they were loading the meat on her and suddenly backed the length of the lead rope.

"My gun," John yelled, lunging forward.

Too late. The horse had knocked it over. John winced as the animal's hoof cracked down on the stock.

"What a shame!" Split exclaimed.

"And I was going to get another deer." Frowning, John picked up his useless gun. The stock was snapped off. "One deer doesn't go far cut up among the boys in the shop and I wanted some steaks for Uncle Mose."

"Take my gun, John. I'll go back to camp and hang up the meat and catch some trout for supper." Split handed John his gun. "It's a little rusty," he added apologetically. "In fact it's so rusty inside that the shell sticks after you shoot. That doesn't make any difference to me, for I always get my game on the first shot. It's a mighty fine gun. You sold it to me."

John looked down at the worst rusted gun he had ever seen.

"I have a little invention of my own to take out the empty shell," Split went on. "I sawed the head off a bolt and sharpened one end like a screw driver. Here it is." He pulled out a six-inch spike of steel from his pocket. "All you have to do is drop this into the muzzle a few times. That loosens the shell. Then poke it out with the sharp end."

John grinned as he dropped Split's invention in his pocket.

He was on top of a ridge where the ground was rather flat and wooded with scattered trees. Happily he hunted on by himself. Matt was right. A hunting trip was what he needed. All problems of the drawing board and the forge had vanished.

With his quick, light step he zigzagged through the trees on the eastern edge of the ridge. Though he covered a good deal of ground he saw not a sign of a deer.

Golden light sifted through the trees. He noticed that the shadows had lengthened. It must be almost suppertime. The thought of trout sizzling in the pan made his mouth water. He decided to circle back on the western ridge. It would be shorter.

He stepped around a great pile of rocks and gasped. The world seemed on fire. The western sky flamed red and gold. The distant lake, the rocks, the peaks, the trees, were the same blazing colors.

Entranced, John sat down on a rock. He forgot all about deer or supper. The moving colors thrilled him in the same way that organ music in church sometimes sang through him. He slowly turned his head from left to right to take in the whole vast, glorious picture.

Then his heart missed a beat. Not a hundred yards away a bear stood on a high rock. John had never seen a grizzly before but he knew this was a grizzly. It was a huge creature, a magnificent specimen. John caught his breath. "The chance of a lifetime," he gasped. "The prize trophy of the Rocky Mountains." And its left side was toward him—a perfect target.

He raised Split's old gun. Like Split, he always got his game on the first shot. This time he didn't dare fail. He aimed coolly, confidently. Then slowly lowered his gun.

The bear was facing west. There was something in the great, motionless figure that reminded John of somebody praying.

They say animals can't see color, he thought.

I wonder. That bear feels about the sunset exactly as I do.

John watched the red clouds darken, the golden light fade. The bear watched them too. When a gray veil floated over sky and mountains John slipped away.

"Good-by, old fellow," he whispered. "May you live to be a hundred."

He wouldn't mention the grizzly to Split, he decided, striding back to camp. I've been a gunmaker and a hunter all my life, he thought. I can never explain to anybody why I couldn't shoot the bear. But I couldn't. Watching the sunset together seemed to make us brothers.

XV

Automatic Guns

"Game is not so plentiful in the mountains as when we were boys, John," Matt remarked as the brothers tramped through the marshes west of Ogden, "but I believe we've never had more water fowl. Mallard, baldpate, teal, pintail, wood duck—I saw them all today."

John did not answer. He had felt the usual thrill of excitement as the great flocks of ducks had soared and wheeled in noisy circles over his head. His gun, a new model with a device not yet patented, had responded with swift precision. Beside him, his dog had lain quiet, and then at his signal had bounded from their hiding place in the long grass to pick up the downed birds without disturbing a feather. The big pockets of his hunting coat bulged with game. It had been a perfect hunt, but all he could think of was the way the long grasses had flattened out in front of the muzzle of his gun as though swept by a strong wind every time a shot was fired.

"There's waste power there," he murmured.

"What do you mean?" Matt asked.

John chuckled. "I don't know—yet," he answered, "but I'm thinking about it."

He kept on thinking about it.

Ogden in the eighties had changed from a frontier village of neatly placed huts and cabins to a pretty town of comfortable homes and gardens on streets shaded by elms, cottonwoods and poplars. The territory of Utah was progressing rapidly. By 1885, all the grazing lands were occupied by fine herds. Mining, especially of copper, was becoming important. The raising of sheep and sugar beets on a big scale were new occupations and Ogden had a canning factory. Pioneer days were gone. No longer could a man walk over to the canyon any day, any season, any hour, and shoot a deer and all the birds he wanted. Some laws restricting the taking of game had been passed. In Ogden, a trapshooting club had been organized for enthusiastic marksmen. Naturally the Browning brothers were expert trapshooters.

In trapshooting, saucers of clay, called clay pigeons, are sprung into the air, one by one, from a trap. The shooter does not know at what angle the "pigeons" will fly. It takes great skill to hit the flying targets.

One day in 1889, John Browning, at a shooting match at the club, was so absorbed in thought that his name had to be called twice when it was his turn to shoot. Standing under an arching green bough he shot perfectly as usual. "It happens every time," he muttered.

He was not referring to his score. He was watching the swaying of the leaves near the muzzle of the gun after every shot was fired. It was the same energy he had noticed stirring the marsh grasses. It's caused, I believe, by the expanding gases from the explosion of the powder, he thought. And it is wasted in the air. It should be used to perform some of the work of the gun.

He went straight to his shop and began to experiment.

First he drilled a hole in a four-inch square of iron which weighed about five pounds. The hole was big enough for a bullet to go through. When he shot through the hole, the gas pressure that followed the bullet blew his five-pound piece of iron some distance from the muzzle. "Good!" he exclaimed. His eyes sparkled. It might take a long time but he was sure that he could harness this gas pressure to make a gas-operated automatic gun. Within a month he had developed his first model.

Through further experiments he produced in 1890 the first model of the military weapon that was to make him world-famous, the machine gun. He demonstrated it before some military officers and officials of the Colt company at Colt's Fire Arms Company in Hartford, Connecticut.

"A crude model," murmured one of the officers, inspecting the machine gun before it was fired. It bore marks of anvil and forge. A web belt made by John Hoxer, a tentmaker in Ogden, held the cartridges.

"It doesn't look promising to me either," said another. "Is this supposed to be fully automatic?" he asked the inventor.

"It is fully automatic," Browning said calmly. "This machine gun starts shooting at the pressure of the trigger and shoots continuously so long as it has ammunition and the pressure is held. Ready, gentlemen?"

The gun fired continuously 1,800 rounds of ammunition in a little more than three minutes.

For a moment the spectators were silent. Then they burst into cheers.

From this model, Browning developed his 1895 machine gun and arranged for its manufacture by Colt.

On his first gas-operated machine he placed a cap

on the muzzle of the barrel. Just as he had made a hole in the square of iron in his first experiment, he bored a hole in the cap through which a bullet could pass. A bracket kept the cap a short distance from the muzzle and formed a small gas chamber.

A cartridge, containing a bullet (lead) and powder, has a metal case. The machine gun was fed ammunition from a belt filled with cartridges. When a shot was fired, the expanding gases which followed the bullet forced pressure against the cap. The cap, connected with the action by a series of rods and levers, went forward. This forward action of the cap started the mechanism which ejected the cartridge case and reloaded the gun automatically.

"The Colt gun is exceedingly simple in construction," began a Navy report on the early machine gun. The Navy ordered fifty of these "Colts" at once.

"John's machine gun is the first fully automatic weapon our government has ever bought," Ed Browning told a customer proudly.

"The only thing the least like it is the Gatling gun," Sam added, "and that is operated by a crank that you have to turn by hand."

"What do you mean by fully automatic?" asked the customer.

"I mean automatic, not semi-automatic," Ed answered. "Often people say automatic when they refer to the semi-automatic. An automatic gun fires steadily so long as it has ammunition and you press the trigger. Now in a semi-automatic, you have to press the trigger anew for every shot."

Browning's automatic machine gun was to prove its value in the Spanish-American War in 1898. Two years later the United States Marines used it to protect Americans in an uprising in China called the Boxer Rebellion. The machine gun is for the use of military and law enforcement agents only. Possession of an automatic weapon by an individual is against the law in the United States.

Watching the movement of the leaves and grasses in front of his gun led Browning to design his first gas-operated machine gun. Later he was to invent machine guns of another type. In the machine gun he had again invented a new, effective weapon and again it did not bear his name.

This did not disturb John Browning. He was too busy inventing. In the same year that the machine gun was sold to Colt he invented a semi-automatic pistol operating on the "recoil principle," quite different in construction from his machine gun. He demonstrated it to Mr. J. H. Hall, president of the Colt company, and Mr. C. J. Ehbets, another official, July 3, 1895.

"Fine," said Mr. Hall at the end of the test. "Of course we want it."

"You are a genius, Mr. Browning," said Mr. Ehbets.

Delighted with the encouragement at the Colt factory he sent a model of his semi-automatic pistol to Belgium, long famous for good guns. In 1898 a representative of Fabrique Nationale d'Armes de Guerre (National Factory of Arms of War) at Liège, Belgium, came all the way to the United States to arrange with the Brownings for the manufacture of the pistols abroad. It was agreed that the pistols would be manufactured by Colt in this country and by FN (Fabrique Nationale) in Europe. The enthusiastic Belgians had their first Brownings on sale the following year, some months before Colt produced theirs.

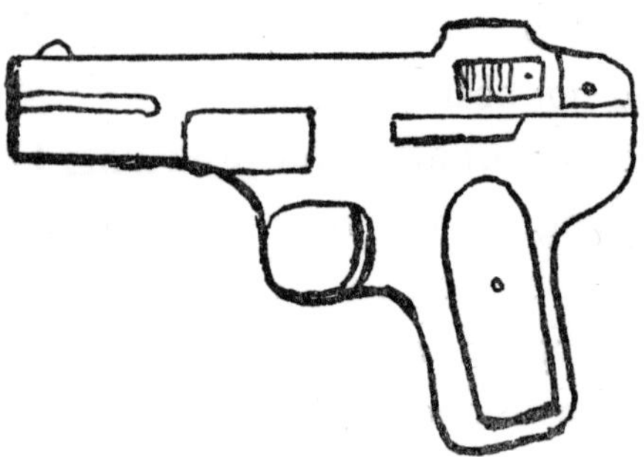

Model 1900, .32 Caliber Semi-Automatic Pistol Manufactured by F.N. and Colt

XVI

Masterpiece

Browning's inventive genius seemed unlimited. He worked steadily. While he was developing his automatic gas-operated machine gun and his semi-automatic pistols he did not neglect the interest closest to his heart, sporting guns.

Perhaps best known of these was a Winchester rifle of the year 1894. Of a list of Browning-designed models introduced by Winchester in the nineties, the most famous was the lever-action Model 94, sometimes called the Winchester .30-30 because it was made to use the .30-30 cartridges especially developed for it. This was the first repeating-action rifle adapted to the new smokeless cartridges.

"Look at my new Winchester," said a western

rancher to a trapper. "Best gun I ever had. It's a .30-30."

"That's too small a load for me," the trapper said. "Game isn't so easy to get any more. It's more wary and there's not so much as there used to be. I need a gun with a longer range."

"This has it," the rancher declared. "These new little smokeless cartridges in this rifle have the force of the old, black powder. You try it."

The trapper tried the gun and rode by mule sixty-five miles to town to buy a Winchester .30-30. Two weeks later he was telling a sheep herder, "Look at my new Winchester. Best gun I ever had. It's a .30-30."

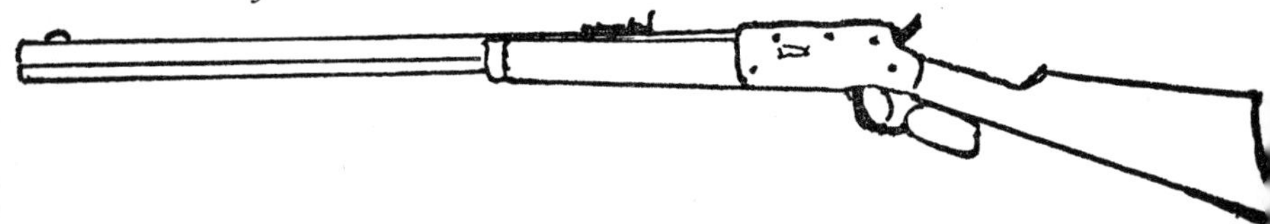

Model 1894 Lever Action Repeating Rifle or the "Winchester .30-30"

Model 94, the Winchester .30-30, became the favorite gun in western cabin, ranch house and miner's hut. As recently as 1958, Winchester advertised it as "the most popular hunting rifle ever built—bar none." The West bought it, not knowing that it was designed by a lanky Westerner named Browning.

Years later one of John Browning's sons* asked him, "How many guns would you have invented if your father had been wealthy?"

"Not one," the inventor answered. "A man may give his days and nights to his work, be proud of it and enjoy it, but it is not fun, not fun such as you had catching trout today. No, I wouldn't have made any guns."

In this he was probably mistaken. Nothing could have kept John Browning from making guns. His imagination had the driving force of a bullet. He went on from one successful invention to another.

In the very year that he was pioneering in making automatic weapons, 1895, he patented another lever-action repeating rifle which was manufactured by Winchester. This was the first gun made to accommodate the heaviest smokeless cartridges being produced. It became a favorite of big-game hunters. President Theodore Roosevelt carried one of these when he went lion hunting in Africa.

In the busy years of the nineties Browning was working also on a special gun problem that presented peculiar difficulties. If he could build an auto-

* John M. Browning was the father of ten children, five sons and five daughters. However, two sons, Leroy and Hugh, died in infancy, and another, Kenneth, was killed in an accident when a young man. His sons, John and Val, and the five daughters are living today (1960).

matic machine gun, why, he asked himself, couldn't he build an autoloading shotgun?

This had never been done. To make a shotgun that would eject the empty case, reload and cock automatically was much more difficult than making an automatic machine gun or rifle because of the nature of shotgun ammunition. The machine gun or rifle uses metallic cartridges of a specific caliber. Not so the shotgun, which uses different powder loads for different game.

Sometimes even Browning wondered if he had undertaken an impossible task.

But fascinated by the problem he worked, tested, rebuilt, experimented, until he gradually came to a solution. In the early hours of a morning in 1900 he finished a model of an autoloading shotgun that satisfied him.

His tired brain whirled. He had spent more time and patience on this than on any other invention. He rubbed a hand across his forehead. The attempts, the disappointments, the failures, the exciting moment when he saw success ahead, all dangled and criss-crossed like cobwebs in his head. He kept thinking of the friction brake and shock absorber he had devised. It could be adjusted so that his autoloader could handle either light or heavy loads. It would eliminate much of the kickback of the gun.

"That gun'll do everything except aim and pull the trigger," he murmured. "I'm proud of it but I wish I could forget it now."

He stood up and stretched his arms, a tall, slim man, forty-five years old with seventeen years of success behind him. He was erect, distinguished-looking, with trim mustache and pointed beard. His hair had thinned revealing a rounded, well-shaped head.

He put on his jacket and a wide-brimmed felt hat, and stepped out into the deserted street.

It was quite dark but the first pink streaks of dawn showed in the east.

"I'm going to clear the cobwebs," he said to himself. He turned eastward.

In a little while he had left the town and was striding through a patch of sagebrush toward Ogden canyon. Now golden light was mingling with pink clouds. Before him shafts of rock of the Wasatch range were touched with pink and gold. Scars and terraces on the mountains were soft, dark purple shadows. "Utah," he recalled, "means 'in the tops of the mountains.'" He smiled remembering his father's disapproval of the name because of its connection with the Utes, the tribe of "high up" Indians. "Pappy was mistaken," he murmured. "The

Indians had a beautiful name for a beautiful land. I'm lucky to live here."

How fresh the cool air smelled. He heard the chirping and flutter of birds waking as the sun rose. A new peace came to him. The cobwebs were gone.

Here the trail was narrow. The canyon walls of rose-colored rock seemed to lean toward him protectingly. The clear blue sky above him seemed close. The familiar peaks of the mountains were old friends looking down on him approvingly in the early morning sunshine.

He thought of his new shotgun with quiet satisfaction. "I have completed my masterpiece," he whispered.

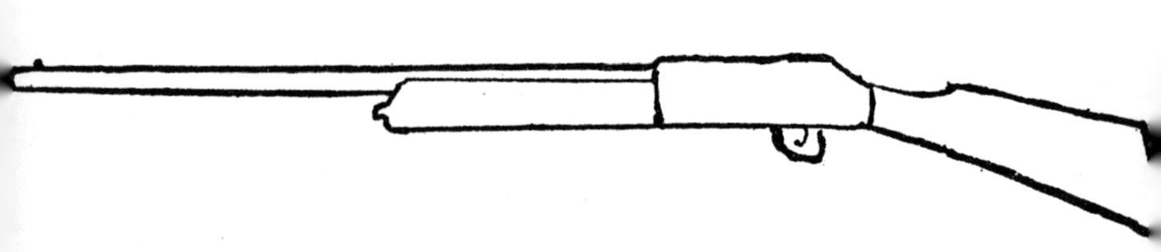

Early Model, Browning Automatic Shotgun

XVII

Going Abroad

October 9, 1900, Browning was granted a patent on his masterpiece, his autoloading or semi-automatic shotgun.

Not long after that Winchester rejected it.

Browning was astounded, incredulous. Not that this was the first time the Winchester company had refused to manufacture one of his designs. He invented and patented his inventions faster than the company could possibly use them. In seventeen years, though they had acquired the patent rights to forty-one Browning patents, they had actually used less than a third of them.

Any change in a factory-made gun requires changes in the machinery which makes its parts. Such changes are expensive. It does not pay to build machinery to make a few guns. To be profitable, there must be mass production over a long period, that is, the machinery must be used for a long time. This is why Winchester had not produced more of his models.

All of this, Browning understood. But not to want his greatest invention, his autoloading shotgun! Why, it represented a revolution in gun design. They had appreciated this but had hesitated. It must be manufactured, he had insisted; and, also, on this remarkable invention he wanted royalties, that is, a sum paid him for every gun sold.

But he had failed to convince them. Perhaps they were afraid it would make some of their popular models appear old-fashioned.

He decided to offer the new design to the Remington Arms Company in Ilion, New York. Organized in the early nineteenth century, Remington was an old and famous company.

An appointment for the afternoon of January 8, 1902, was arranged with the president of Remington, Mr. Marcellus Hartley, at his office in New York City.

Hopefully Browning arrived at the president's office at the appointed time. The president was late. Browning sat in an outer office, his gun model across his knees, waiting. Three times he pulled his heavy gold watch from his pocket.

A door was open to an inner office where Mr. Hartley's secretary, George Bingham, sat at a desk writing in a ledger. From time to time he answered the telephone. The mouthpiece of the phone was at the top of a metal tube which was mounted on a small, round base. The receiver hung on a hook at the side. Browning noticed that he picked it up from the desk when he used it, so the instrument must be quite light.

That would be handy for Matt in the store at home, thought Browning.

In Ogden the telephones hung on the wall.

Again he looked at his watch.

"Do you think he'll be here soon?" he asked the secretary.

"It's not like Mr. Hartley to be late," Bingham answered. "I'm sorry, Mr. Browning, I have no idea what—" The ring of the phone interrupted.

The young man's face turned pale as he listened to the message. "Oh, no," he gasped.

He put the receiver on the hook and stared wide-eyed at Browning. "Mr. Hartley won't be here soon," he said. His voice broke. "He won't be here —ever."

The president of the Remington company had died a few minutes earlier of a heart attack.

Shocked, disappointed, grieved for the friends and

family of this man he had not known, Browning walked the crowded streets of New York downhearted as he had never been before. The clatter of horses' hoofs, the rattle of wheels, shouts of drivers, rush of the elevated trains, made a nerve-racking clamor. Though the streets were much wider than a canyon trail, the tall buildings seemed to press in upon him. The gray mist from the Hudson and the smoke of a million chimneys floated above him. The sky seemed far away. He walked among more people than he would see in a year in Ogden and never felt more lonely.

Without plan he walked, not knowing where he was going. Through the mist a great white wall rose before him. It was the hull of a ship. He had wandered toward a pier. Here was a steamer, a ship to take him across the ocean. He made his decision suddenly. He would take his invention to the place where fine guns were appreciated. Why, FN in Belgium had beat Colt in getting his pistols on the market, he remembered. FN would want his masterpiece. He would go to Belgium.

At the Fabrique Nationale D'Armes de Guerre in Liège, Belgium, there was no hesitation. Browning's automatic shotgun was welcomed with enthusiasm. And like his pistol that the Belgians manufactured, it would bear his name.

Back in New York, the young grandson of the late Mr. Hartley was made president of Remington. He was eager to manufacture Browning's semi-automatic guns, and soon made a contract with the Browning brothers under which the manufacturer agreed to pay the Brownings a royalty on every gun made, instead of buying the patent outright. John Browning himself supervised the manufacture of the guns at the Remington plant in Ilion, New York. They appeared in 1905, the first autoloading shotguns in America!

In Belgium also, Browning was to receive royalties on the guns instead of selling the patent rights. This marked the beginning of a long and happy association between FN and the Brownings.

XVIII

Pistols and Honors

Although sporting guns were Browning's chief interest, his pistols brought him the most recognition. Colt manufactured his pistols in this country and FN made them for all markets outside the United States. The Belgian police promptly adopted the Browning and were followed in their choice by the police in other European countries. A later model was chosen as the official side arm of the Swedish army. Some Brownings were manufactured by Swedish government arsenals. The Ministry of War in France sent Browning congratulations on his wonderful pistol. In the United States, a Browning-designed .45 caliber pistol manufactured by Colt became the official military side arm.

"What do you think of this, Matt?" Browning

asked his brother one morning. "The city of Philadelphia wants to honor me."

Matt's grin spread wide as he read the letter John Browning gave him. The Franklin Institute had recommended the inventor to receive the John Scott Medal awarded to "the most deserving."

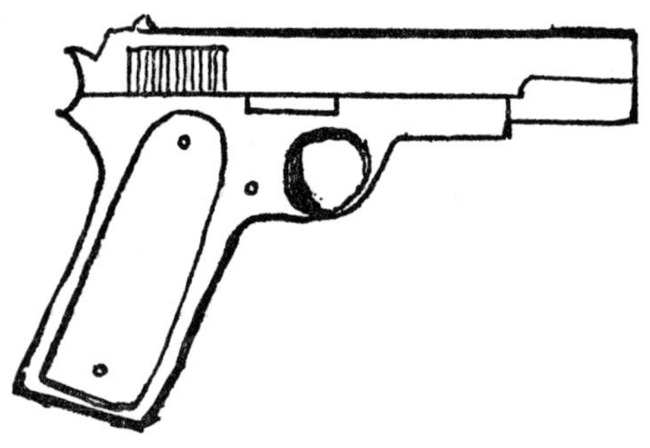

Government .45 Caliber Automatic

The medal was presented to Browning in 1905. On one side of it were the words, *Awarded by the City of Philadelphia;* on the other, *John M. Browning for his automatic pistols.*

In this field he was a pioneer. A few designs for such pistols had been developed and some in small quantities had been manufactured. All proved awkward and clumsy. Brownings were the first successful semi-automatic pistols.

Through the nineties and the first years of this

century patent after patent was issued to John Browning for pistol designs. Sometimes two and three patents for pistols were granted in one year. Each patent represented long periods of painstaking work.

His pistols varied in size and pattern. They were of different calibers, .32, .38 or .45. Some were hammerless. Some had an exposed hammer. Some ejected cartridges from the top and some from the side. He tried different locks, slides and various lengths of barrels. He worked constantly to make his pocket pistol so simply constructed that it could be easily taken apart and as easily "assembled" or put together again.

There was this difference between his pistols manufactured by Colt and by FN. For many years the Colt pistols were marked *Browning patent* in addition to COLT, but they were known as Colts. Those made in Belgium were called Brownings. Abroad, Brownings became so famous that the word appears in the French dictionary as a common noun.

"Browning" says one French dictionary "(from the name of the inventor) a magazine arm replacing the revolver. Also called Browning Automatic pistol."

When the millionth Browning was manufactured by FN in 1912, John M. Browning was invited to

Belgium for a celebration. Under brilliant crystal chandeliers important men, including the King of Belgium, assembled at a banquet to honor the inventor. To ringing applause he was presented the millionth Browning.

The orchestra began to play "The Star-Spangled Banner" as a drapery was slowly drawn from a bronze statue, the work of a famous French sculptor. The statue was a surprise to Browning. He was now a man of fifty-seven, bald and with a gray mustache, but sudden tears glittered in his blue eyes. "If Pappy could know this," flashed into his mind. The statue represented the genius of John Browning.

Among the men standing in his honor the distinguished-looking, six-foot-three inventor towered as his inventive genius towered above the talent of all gunmakers in the world.

Then came the climax of the evening. King Albert of Belgium came forward to confer a title upon him. An elaborate medal showing a cross on a wreath of laurel and a crown above it was pinned over his heart. This was the cross of a Chevalier de l'Ordre de Léopold (Knight of the Order of Leopold). John Moses Browning, gunmaker of Ogden, Utah, was now a gentleman with a European title.

Such honors made little difference to him. He went home to his old workshop and went to work.

"When people talk about genius I think of you, Matt," he said one day. "You're a banker and interested in ranching, mines, the sugar industry, coal, railroads—everything, and you make everything pay. Yet, like Pappy, you've taken time to do a lot for the community. And of course, have always run our gun business wonderfully. You're the family genius! How do you manage to do it all?"

Matt beamed. "Remember, John," he answered, "you've given me something good to manage."

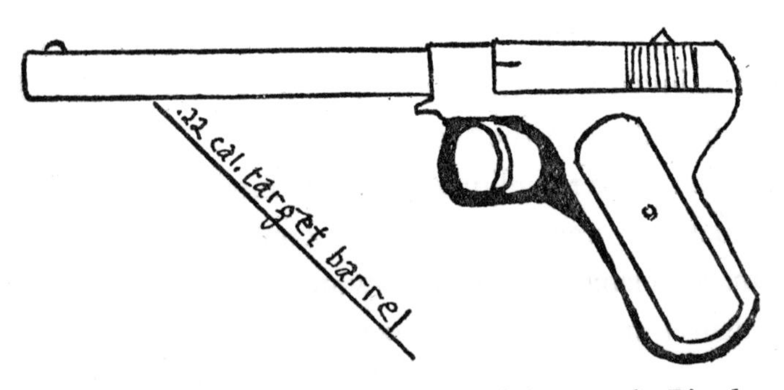

The Woodsman .22 Caliber Semi-Automatic Pistol

XIX

War

There was one flaw in Browning's first machine gun. It fired so fast it got too hot. In the test at Colt's back in 1890 the barrel had glowed a luminous blue from the intense firing. In a later model Browning tried to remedy the defect by using a heavier barrel. This was only a partial solution besides making the gun heavier than was desirable.

He would have continued to work on the machine gun if anybody had been interested in it, but the machine gun is a military weapon and therefore was overlooked in the early nineteen hundreds. In the happy, safe years following the short and successful conflict with Spain, the United States was unconcerned about military preparedness. To be sure, Germany was piling up munitions and improving machine guns, but "Germany is a military nation, different from us," Americans assured each other. "It is the nature of Germans to admire the army. That does not mean that they are going to use it. Anyway, with the ocean between us, we wouldn't be involved if there was a European war."

So John Browning put aside his machine guns and devoted himself to other arms.

Early in 1917 Americans began to be afraid that the United States would be drawn into the terrible war which had raged in Europe for three years. Our country was not prepared for war. Most of its machine guns were the old-fashioned Browning Model 95's made more than twenty years before. The United States Government sent a plea to gun designers for a new and more effective machine gun. Of course, when the date was set for a competition of new models in Washington, Browning had one ready. He also offered a new automatic rifle.

Three hundred people assembled to see the gun demonstration on Congress Heights near Washington, D. C., February 27, 1917. In the crowd were representatives of Great Britain, France, Belgium and Italy.

"We know Brownings in Europe," said a Frenchman. "Is the inventor of these new automatic weapons the same man who designed the pistols?"

"The same man," said a Belgian.

"Then I am hopeful," an Italian remarked. "Ah, this must be the great inventor himself."

People were shaking hands with tall John Browning as he approached, carrying his brand-new automatic rifle. It was gas operated and air cooled. Its cartridges were contained in a magazine attached under the breech.

"This gun," Browning explained, "can be fired from the shoulder or the hip. By this lever it can be adjusted to become semi-automatic or fully automatic."

In the test, the magazine, containing 20 rounds of ammunition, was emptied in two and a half seconds. In the next two and a half seconds Browning detached the old magazine and fitted on the new one. The gun fired 480 rounds per minute.

The crowd gasped. It was wonderful, incredible.

"That will give us the 'walking fire' we need," said an Army officer.

"It is just what we've been looking for," said another.

The B.A.R. (Browning Automatic Rifle) was

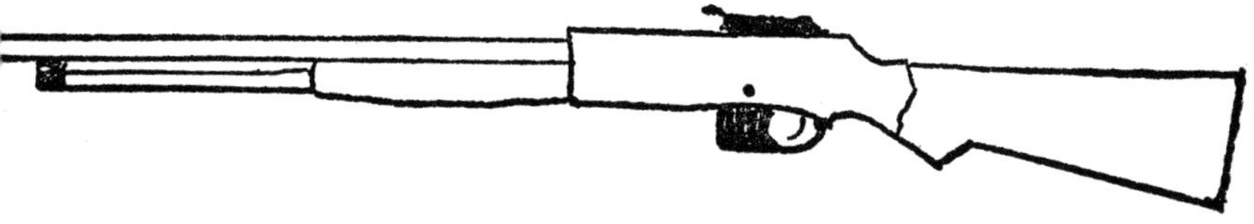

Browning Automatic Rifle (B.A.R.)

immediately adopted and three different factories in the United States were ordered to manufacture it.

During the war, 52,000 B.A.R.'s were shipped abroad and the first man to fire a B.A.R. in action was the gallant Lieutenant Val A. Browning, John Browning's son.

The other gun which Browning brought to the competition was his Heavy Water-Cooled Machine Gun of .30 caliber. This 1917 machine gun, unlike his first machine gun, was operated on the recoil principle which he had used successfully in his pistols. It fired even faster than the old model. To keep the barrel from becoming too hot, the barrel was encased in a jacket of water.

In the test the gun performed well. However, because of the rough treatment it would receive in

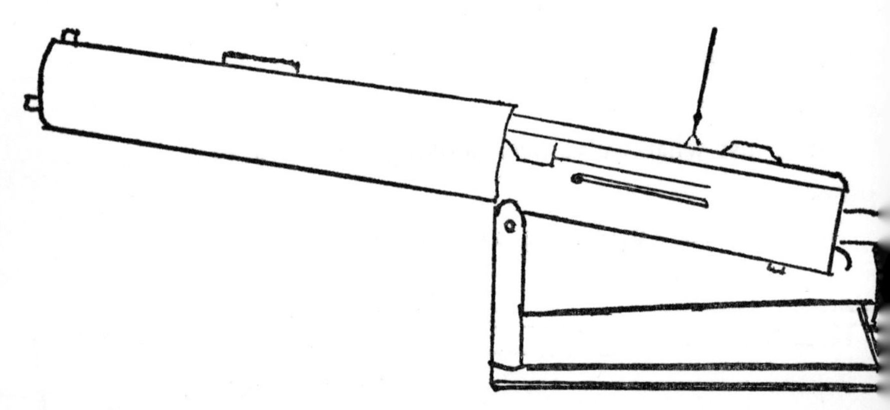

Browning's Model of His 1917 .30 Caliber Water Cooled Machine Gun

warfare, the officers wanted to see more tests before they adopted it.

In a little over a month, April 6, 1917, the United States declared war, and in May the Browning Heavy Water-Cooled Machine Gun was tested again. It fired perfectly 20,000 rounds at a rate of 600 per minute. Some thought this was too good to be true. They suspected that Browning had built a model especially for demonstration. He called for a second model. The second gun was even better. It fired continuously for 48 minutes and 12 seconds. All who saw the demonstration were enthusiastic over the Browning machine gun.

The board to select arms appointed by the Secretary of War reported that the Browning Heavy .30 caliber model and the already accepted B.A.R. were "the most effective guns of their type known to the members."

Shortly after the .30 caliber machine guns arrived in France, General John Pershing, in command of the American forces, asked for a heavier machine gun to use against armored tanks. He wanted a more powerful, but not a heavier, machine gun. This presented a big problem in gun designing.

Within a year John Browning had his .50 Caliber Water-Cooled Machine Gun ready to demonstrate. In it he had placed an "oil buffer" which absorbed some of the force of the recoil and so reduced the strain on parts. It also provided a means of controlling the rate of fire.

Again he went to Washington with a machine gun. Again a crowd assembled at Congress Heights. Again people called the inventor a genius. At the close of the successful tests reporters crowded around him.

"This is a miracle," said one. "How do you account for it, Mr. Browning?"

With pencils poised over their notebooks, the reporters waited for his answer.

Browning's blue eyes twinkled. He said, "One drop of genius in a barrel of sweat wrought this miracle."

Another achievement of Browning's was the reduction in weight of his .30 caliber machine gun from 37 to 22 pounds while increasing its rate of fire. This was the first gun in our country to be mounted in an airplane so that the pilot could aim the gun while maneuvering the plane. The firing mechanism was timed so that the pilot could fire between the blades of the propeller as it turned.

Makers of guns are sometimes accused of encouraging war in order to sell their product. Nobody could ever say this about John Browning. He went to the rescue of his country without mentioning money. His machine guns, rifles and pistols were officially adopted by the United States for use in World War I. Many arms factories and some factories which had never before manufactured arms were tooled to produce Browning guns for the war. Production of his guns had reached its peak before anything was said about payment to Browning.

When the government official authorized to make him an offer began to discuss a financial agreement, he observed, "I know, Mr. Browning, that this will be only a fraction of what you would receive as royalties on your guns under ordinary circumstances." The agreement asked full rights to manufacture machine guns, rifles and .45 automatic pistols. It also required that Browning give his personal supervision to their production. Payment offered by our government for all this was less than a tenth usually paid as royalties on the guns.

Without the slightest hesitation Browning said, "Gentlemen, if that suits Uncle Sam, it's all right with me."

Newton D. Baker, Secretary of War, wrote promptly, November 13, 1917, thanking him for his "patriotic and generous attitude." "You have performed as you must realize," he wrote, "a very distinct service to the country in these inventions, and contributed to the strength and effectiveness of our armies. You have added to that service by the attitude you have taken in the financial arrangements necessary to make your inventions available to the Government."

Praise for the Brownings came from the battlefields. The guns were fast, strong, reliable. An officer of the 79th Division, the first to use Brownings abroad, reported, "The guns became rusty on the outside due to the rain and the wet weather, but in every instance when the guns were called upon to fire, they fired perfectly." Assistant Secretary of War Benedict Crowell in a book on munitions wrote, "Both types of Brownings proved to be unqualified successes in actual battle."

Our country owes much to Browning, the gunmaker.

XX

His Last Gun

Joyously the United States celebrated the end of the fighting of World War I, November 11, 1918. Our country had been in the war only one year, seven months and five days. The improved arms she brought her allies had been a big help. Without John Browning the end might not have been so soon or so happy.

Now the United States felt sure that she had fought a war to end all wars. "Sink the battleships; scrap the guns," was the hopeful cry. "There will never be another war."

John Browning did not agree. "There will be another war," he predicted, "and the skies will swarm with warriors." He thought that the country should have on hand the latest kind of weapons and not again "have to pay the terrific price of trying to do in a few months what other nations have spent years in doing."

For a few years the Army Ordnance Department continued its interest in weapons. In November 1920, the Chief of the Aircraft Armament Design asked Browning to inspect a model of a cannon to be mounted on an airplane. Army engineers had worked on it for some time and the work was not going well.

No wonder. The basic design was no good, Browning decided. "Abandon it," was his advice to a group of officers.

General Williams, Chief of Ordnance, looked anxiously at Mr. Fred T. Moore, production manager of Colt's who had also been asked to inspect the model.

"I agree with Mr. Browning," said Mr. Moore.

"Then, Mr. Browning, won't you design us a cannon for use on airplanes?" General Williams asked.

"I'm too busy," Browning protested.

At sixty-five, the age when many men retire, he was busy as usual.

"You're the only man in the country who could do this," General Williams insisted.

"That's right," Moore said.

"And we need it," added an officer.

Browning agreed to think about it.

Early the next year he had an aircraft cannon model ready for the Army, and shortly after that he made two more. All three were successful.

But again the country was trying to avoid war by avoiding weapons. Blind to conditions in Europe which would lead to more fighting, the United States frowned upon military preparedness. The drawings of these cannons and the models were filed away by the Army. Later they were useful in World War II, fifteen years after the death of their inventor.

Sons of the Browning brothers had now joined their fathers in business. John and Val, sons of John M. Browning, and Marriner, son of Matt, were officers in the Browning Arms Company and in the J. M. Browning and M. S. Browning Company. The Brownings had offices in St. Louis as well as Ogden. The family business was devoted to selling Browning guns, manufactured both here and abroad, to improving them and to adding new guns.

In 1925 Browning was designing a new type of sporting gun. It was double-barreled with one barrel placed on top or superposed on the other. Browning called it "the superposed shotgun," but most people later called it the Browning "over and under."

One morning he frowned over a letter from FN

which was to manufacture the new gun the next year. FN wanted him to come there to supervise the production of his first superposed shotguns.

How I miss Matt, he thought sadly, folding the letter. He wished he could talk this over with his brother. Matt had died two years before.

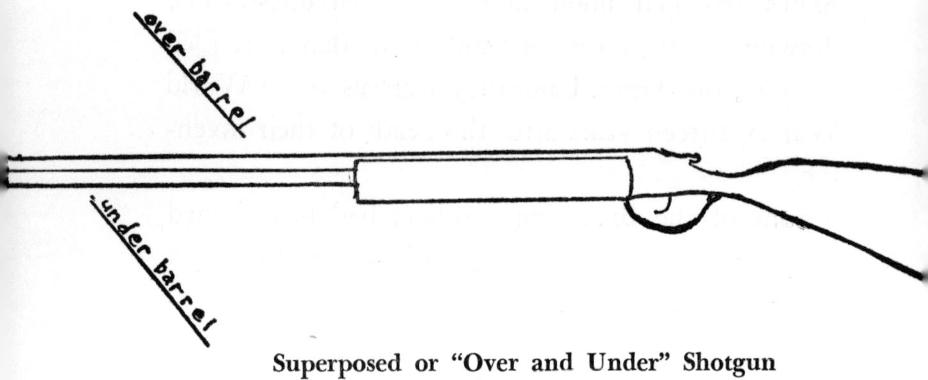

Superposed or "Over and Under" Shotgun

John Browning was now seventy. It was a long trip to Liège from Ogden, he reflected. His son Val could do the job as well as he could. Val had supervised at FN and was an inventor. He was deeply interested in the superposed too. Browning looked down at the new model and felt a thrill of excitement. A good gun! It was to be a "take down" model, that is, it could be quickly taken down into two parts. The stock and action would be in one part and the fore end and the barrels in the other.

"That will be handy for storage or shipment," he muttered, smiling. At seventy, he felt the same satisfaction over a good gun that he had felt at seventeen. "But I must see that they—" Already he was thinking of directions that must be given.

He went to Belgium.

While there he was stricken with a sudden heart attack, and died November 26, 1926. He had led a busy life; he was busy to the end. His death at seventy-one marked the loss to the world of the greatest gun inventor who had ever lived.

A United States military guard of honor met the boat which bore his body home. Great men all over the world mourned the death of "the father of modern firearms." The Secretary of War, Dwight F. Davis, spoke of the handicap to the future development of automatic weapons without him. "Nobody," he said, "has contributed so much to the national security of our country as Mr. Browning."

In the summer of 1960, thirty-four years after the death of John M. Browning, a boy from St. Louis, Missouri, was visiting his cousin in Ogden, Utah.

At the breakfast table the Ogden boy said to his guest, "Ronnie, you'll want to see our museum."

"I doubt it," said Ronnie in a bored tone. "After

all, Carl, I've been to most of the famous museums in the East."

Carl's cheeks flushed. "The Browning Arms Collection is famous too. Aren't you interested in guns?"

"Of course, but the Browning Arms Company is in St. Louis," Ronnie answered.

"Oh, no!" exclaimed Carl. "It's right here in Ogden where it's always been."

"You're both right," said Carl's father, looking up from his newspaper. "Today descendants of John M. Browning carry on the business and it is worldwide. The Browning Arms Company has offices not only in Ogden and St. Louis but also in Montreal, Canada, and Liège, Belgium."

"But the guns must be made in St. Louis," Ronnie persisted.

"No," Carl's father explained. "The Browning Arms Company does not have a manufacturing plant in this country, though here in Ogden the company has a research organization. The family business is devoted to selling Browning guns. The Fabrique Nationale d'Armes de Guerre in Belgium is one of the biggest factories in the world making small arms and its chief output consists of firearms invented by John M. Browning."

"I remember now," said Ronnie. "Father has a

Browning 'over and under' and a 'sweet sixteen' and both of them were made in Belgium."

Carl's father nodded. "Many Browning guns are shipped to this country. In the Arms Collection you'll see the original models that John N. Browning himself made of some of his most famous guns."

"Of course, if it's that kind of a museum," said Ronnie, "I want to see it."

A little later the two boys walked toward an impressive, new brick building. It was long for its height, with a flat roof and many windows in the modern style.

" 'John M. Browning,' " Ronnie read the words on the front. "It's bigger than I expected," he added.

"The building is the new armory for our Utah National Guard," Carl explained, "and it is named in honor of Browning. The museum's inside with a lot of his most interesting guns. You know the finest museums in the country wanted the Browning Arms Collection before this memorial was built."

"I should think so." Ronnie's eyes sparkled as he stepped into the museum. "That is, if these are the original models."

"Most of them are," said Carl, leading the way. "Here's the first rifle he patented, the one that started Browning's career. And you mustn't miss the three models of the automatic shotgun he took to Belgium. Each is an original model. And oh, the lathe that belonged to his father. He brought it from Iowa in a covered wagon drawn by oxen."

"There's so much to see," said Ronnie.

"Yes, there are even his father's old repeating rifles and the decoration the King of Belgium gave Browning and a medal from Philadelphia!"

The boys spent all morning in the museum. Models of Browning's first patented gun, the single-shot rifle, and his last one, the superposed shotgun, and many guns invented in the years between these two models, were on exhibition. Sporting guns, pistols and machine guns were represented.

"He did so much," exclaimed Ronnie.

"Yet this doesn't include everything he did. Father says that one hundred and twenty-eight patents were issued to John M. Browning. Think of it!"

"He was the greatest gunmaker in the world!" Ronnie agreed.

The boys were leaving the armory when Ronnie observed thoughtfully, "As you go from one model to another you can see how he kept thinking of some new gimmick to make a gun better, can't you?"

But this memorial exhibit is more than a record of achievement in firearms. It is the record of the triumph of an individual. It shows how much can be accomplished by perseverance and work added to native ability. John M. Browning was not helped by wealth or superior education. Unimpressed by fame, not desirous of riches, the boy born in a frontier village stayed there and won both.

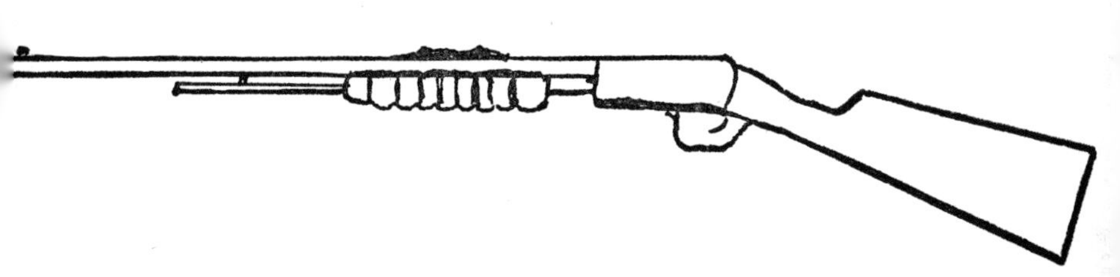

Trombone Action .22 Caliber Repeating Rifle, Patented 1922, Manufactured by F.N.

CATALOGUE
of Some Representative Browning Guns
(*Chronological Order*)

RIFLES

1. WINCHESTER MODEL 85 SINGLE SHOT RIFLE

Browning's first invention to be manufactured. Introduced in the Winchester catalogue of 1885.

2. WINCHESTER MODEL 86 LEVER ACTION REPEATING RIFLE

Favorite of big-game hunters. Cartridges carried in tubular magazine under the barrel. Appeared in 1886; modified in 1936 and issued as Model 71; continued until 1958, a period of seventy-four years.

3. WINCHESTER MODEL 87 SHOTGUN, LEVER ACTION REPEATING SHOTGUN

Though Colt, Roper, and Spencer had each manufactured a repeating shotgun before this, Browning's model was the first successful one. A favorite in this country until early in the twentieth century.

4. WINCHESTER MODEL 90 PUMP ACTION RIFLE

First pump or slide action rifle manufactured by Winchester. Widely used for small game and target shooting, especially in Great Britain where shooting galleries came to be called "Winchester Rifle Ranges."

5. WINCHESTER MODEL 1892 LEVER ACTION REPEATING RIFLE

Made for smaller-caliber cartridges than Model 86. Popular. In 1932 Winchester presented a model of this gun engraved with the serial number 1,000,000 to the Honorable Patrick J. Hurley, Secretary of War.

6. WINCHESTER MODEL 93 PUMP ACTION REPEATING SHOTGUN, MODIFIED IN 1897 TO A "TAKE-DOWN" TYPE, THE WELL-KNOWN MODEL 97

First shotgun with pump action listed by Winchester.

A short-barrel variation of this shotgun was widely used as a riot gun by police. The American Express Company at one time armed its messengers with it. Used with such effectiveness by American troops in trench warfare in World War I that the enemy officially protested the use of shotguns by the American army.

7. WINCHESTER MODEL 94, BETTER KNOWN AS THE "WINCHESTER .30-30"

First lever action repeating rifle adapted to handle smokeless cartridges. In great demand, especially in the West.

8. WINCHESTER MODEL 95 LEVER ACTION REPEATING RIFLE

Handled all the heaviest cartridges. Used for big game in North America and Africa. Used by

Theodore Roosevelt and other famous hunters. Manufactured in carbine and musket as well as sporting rifle. Used by the United States Army in the Spanish-American War. Discontinued in 1931 after the manufacture of approximately half a million.

9. WINCHESTER MODEL 1900
SINGLE SHOT RIFLE

"Bolt action" containing few parts. Winchester made variations of Model 1900 in 1902, 1904, and 1928. Made further changes in the single shot rifle known today as Models 58, 59, 60, and 68.

10. WINCHESTER THUMB TRIGGER RIFLE

A variation of Model 1900. No trigger or trigger guard. The shooter pressed down on a button behind the cocking piece to release the firing pin.

Never very popular in the United States though extremely so in Australia.

11. MODEL 36 SINGLE SHOT SHOTGUN

Similar to Model 1902 Single Shot Rifle. Only shotgun in the United States chambered for 9 mm paper shot shells. Discontinued in 1927.

12. AUTOMATIC SHOTGUN

Considered by Browning his most difficult invention. Patented in 1900, this autoloading shotgun was first introduced in 1903 by Fabrique Nationale d'Armes de Guerre (F.N.) in Liège, Belgium. In 1905 Remington was licensed to manufacture it as Model 11 and offered it in several gauges.* The

* Gauge is the unit of measure of the bore of a shotgun. It is determined by the number of lead balls required to weigh a pound that can be inserted in the barrel. Thus a sixteen gauge could hold sixteen such balls.

lightweight 16 gauge, popular as the "Sweet Sixteen," is made by F.N.

13. STEVENS MODEL 520 HAMMERLESS PUMP ACTION SHOTGUN

Placed on the market by the Stevens Arms Company in 1904. Especially designed for ease of "take down." Later the same type of gun was manufactured under the Savage name.

14. F.N. .22 CALIBER AUTOMATIC RIFLE (1914–1957)

Really a semi-automatic rifle especially designed to handle the .22 caliber ammunition. Throughout the world a favorite of shooting galleries because ejection of the shell is downward, thus there is no danger of a hot, ejected cartridge striking another shooter.

15. BROWNING AUTOMATIC RIFLE, OR THE "B.A.R."

Invented in 1917. Gas-operated, air-cooled automatic rifle adopted by the United States for use in World War I. After the war, production rights reverted to Colt's Patent Fire Arms Company. In 1920 F.N. was licensed to produce it for Europe.

16. REMINGTON MODEL 17

Repeater-type shotgun introduced by Remington Arms Company in 1921. Hammerless, bottom ejection, pump action, twenty gauge, weight only 5½ pounds. Production discontinued in 1933.

The Ithaca Model 37 pump gun is of this type.

17. REMINGTON MODEL 24 AUTOMATIC RIFLE (1922–1935)

The same as F.N. .22 Caliber Automatic Rifle, item 14 of this catalogue.

18. F.N. 19 TROMBONE .22 CALIBER RIFLE (1922–)

One of the few Browning designs never manufactured or sold in the United States though in continuous production since 1922. Popular in Europe, South America and Canada.

19. SUPERPOSED SHOTGUN (1926–)

Double barrel with barrels mounted one above the other; often called the "over and under." Patented in 1926, the year of Browning's death. First models had double triggers. Single trigger was designed by inventor's son, Val A. Browning, who later made other improvements. Offered in a wide variety of weights, grades, barrel lengths, and chokes. No less than 269 specifications for this model are listed today.

20. REMINGTON MODEL 241 AUTOMATIC RIFLE (1935–1951)

A modified, somewhat heavier version of Remington Model 24.

21. BROWNING SEMI-AUTOMATIC .22 RIFLE (1956–)

This is the Browning Arms Company modern version of John M. Browning's historic semi-automatic .22 rifle described in the preceding items 14, 17, and 20.

MACHINE GUNS

Despite the world-wide fame of his small arms, John M. Browning is perhaps better known in the United States for his invention of the machine gun. An early Browning model of this military weapon was used by United States troops in the Spanish-American War, 1898, and in the Boxer Rebellion in 1900. Later the Browning machine gun was to become of great importance in World War I, 1917–1918, and again in World War II, 1941–1945.

During World War II, nearly two decades after the inventor's death, his machine gun was in such demand that it was made by Colt, Savage, General Motors, Frigidaire, and five other companies. Sixty-six different models of the Browning recoil-operated machine gun were made for the United States and thirteen allies.

No weapon was more respected by the enemy. A German general congratulating another upon a victory was jubilant over the capture of thousands of Browning machine guns just unloaded from an allied convoy. Authorities on warfare have said that the decision of a group of British officers to mount Brownings on their Hurricane Fighters brought about the turning point in World War II. The invention of the machine gun alone would have made Browning's name world-famous.

1. MODEL 1895 AUTOMATIC MACHINE GUN

   Gas operated, manufactured by Colt beginning in 1895. Nicknamed "Potato Digger," and "Browning Peacemaker."

   First fully automatic weapon purchased by the United States forces; used in the Boxer Rebellion in China and in the Spanish-American War in Cuba, 1898.

2. MODEL MACHINE GUN 1901

   Recoil operated. Patented in 1901, but plans were set aside because of lack of interest in military weapons at this time.

3. MODEL 1917 BROWNING HEAVY WATER-COOLED MACHINE GUN, CALIBER .30

First Browning gun to arrive in France in World War I. An improved version of Model 1901. Manufactured during the war by Westinghouse, Remington, and Colt.

4. .50 CALIBER VERSION OF BROWNING WATER-COOLED MACHINE GUN

Developed in 1918 at request of General Pershing for a more powerful machine gun to use against German tanks. An oil buffer was introduced to absorb excess energy of the recoil.

5. BROWNING .30M2

Browning Air-Cooled Model .30 Caliber Machine Gun.

Weight only 22 pounds, rate of fire increased. First weapon to be affixed successfully to pursuit planes with the firing mechanism of the gun synchronized with the motor so that a stream of bullets could pass between the blades of the propeller as it revolved.

6. 37 MM AIRCRAFT CANNON

Completed in 1921 at request of the government for a cannon to mount on aircraft; first of three successful models, each more effective than the last. All were put aside because of lack of interest in military weapons.

In World War II many thousands were used by our allies. Rather generally, our planes preferred the lighter machine gun.

7. BROWNING .50M2

Air-cooled model of the .50 Caliber Browning. Lightened in weight.

The Browning .30M2 and .50M2 were exclusively the aircraft machine guns of the United States during World War II; also used in more recent campaigns.

BROWNING AUTOMATIC PISTOLS

Since John M. Browning designed his first pistol in 1895 it is believed that more semi-automatic pistols of Browning design have been manufactured than of all other patterns in the world combined. Two models were invented in 1895 but never produced commercially because he so quickly made other designs. In 1896 came two others which were the prototypes of the first Colt semi-automatic.

1. F.N. .32 CALIBER M 1900

Invented in 1897. Hammerless; blow-back action. First Browning semi-automatic pistol to be manufactured. Adopted by Belgian police and other law-enforcement and army officers throughout Europe.

This pistol marked the beginning of Browning's association with F.N. Production by F.N. for all countries outside the United States began in 1899. By 1909, 500,000 of this model had been manufactured.

2. COLT .38 CALIBER M 1900

Invented in 1896; submitted to Colt's Patent Fire Arms Company the same year. Exposed hammer; operated on the short recoil principle. First commercially produced semi-automatic pistol in America. Introduced in 1900 as a sporting type; military version, 1902; pocket model, 1903.

3. COLT MODEL 1903 "POCKET" .32 AND .380

Blow-back action principle. Model discontinued in 1946 after nearly a million had been produced.

4. MODEL 1903 MILITARY SEMI-AUTOMATIC PISTOL, OR, IN EUROPE, PISTOLET AUTOMATIC BROWNING GRANDE MODÈLE

Adopted by Sweden as official sidearm. F.N. developed new cartridge for this pistol called the "9 mm Browning long." Pistol manufactured by F.N. and also Swedish Government Arsenals.

5. GOVERNMENT .45 CALIBER AUTOMATIC

Invented in 1905; semi-automatic, short recoil type; adopted by the United States government in 1911, in continuous military service for nearly half a century. Originally produced by Colt, it was manufactured in time of war by Remington, Winchester, Savage, Ithaca, and other companies both here and in Canada.

6. SEMI-AUTOMATIC PISTOL MODEL "VEST POCKET" CALIBER .25

Also invented in 1905; hammerless; blow-back principle; weight only 13 ounces. First manufactured by F.N. in 1905. Within five years approximately 100,000 had been sold. Colt's began production of this model in 1908.

7. BROWNING .25 CALIBER

A modern version of the "vest pocket" described

in item 6. After World War II the Browning Arms Company redesigned the model, making it smaller and lighter.

8. MODELS 1910 AND 1922 BROWNING SEMI-AUTOMATIC

Similar to Model 1900 .32 Caliber described in item 1; new safety modifications; 1922 model an enlarged version of the 1910 introduced by F.N. in 1912; currently produced by the Browning Arms Company.

9. THE "COLT" WOODSMAN, .22 CALIBER SEMI-AUTOMATIC PISTOL

Invented in 1914; widely used as a target pistol; still popular; about one million have been manufactured since 1915.

Though the name of the manufacturer of this model, Colt, is usually attached to the pistol it is another Browning invention patented in his name.

10. SEMI-AUTOMATIC PISTOL 9 MM PARABELLUM

Invented in 1923 in answer to a request from the French Ministry of War for a semi-automatic pistol to use the 9 mm Parabellum cartridge, the same as the 9 mm Luger. Browning invented one on the blow-back principle and one with short recoil-type action; latter was patented after his death. It became the official sidearm of the Belgian army and other European troops. Also called "Browning Model 1935" and the "Browning High Power." Standard military sidearm of the NATO countries. Produced today by the Browning Arms Company.

SOURCES

"A History of Browning Guns from 1831 including Achievements of John M. Browning, 'the Father of Modern Fire Arms' " (pamphlet), Browning Arms Company, copyright 1942

Browning Family Papers

Dictionary of American Biography, Charles Scribner's Sons, New York, copyright by American Council of Learned Societies, 1958

Great Salt Lake, Dale Morgan, Bobbs-Merrill, Indianapolis, New York, copyright 1911

"Gun Master," Chester Newton Hess (article), *Arizona Highways*, November 1953

"Here Is Ogden" (pamphlet), Ogden Chamber of Commerce, Ogden, Utah, 1960

Jedediah Smith and the Opening of the West, Dale Morgan, Bobbs-Merrill, Indianapolis, New York, copyright 1953

"John M. Browning Armory" (pamphlet), Browning Arms Company, copyright 1959

"Ogden," Bernard De Voto, in *Taming of the Frontier* (27–60) Minton, copyright 1925

"Ogden Welcomes You" (pamphlet), Ogden Chamber of Commerce, Ogden, Utah, 1960

Remington Arms in American History, Alden Hatch, Rinehart and Company, New York, copyright 1911

Salt the Fifth Element, Garnett T. Eskew, J. C. Ferguson and Associates, copyright 1948

Statistical Data on Ogden, Ogden Chamber of Commerce, Ogden, Utah, 1960

The City of the Saints, Richard F. Burton, Longmans Green and Company, New York, copyright 1862

The Machine Gun, George M. Chinn, Lieutenant Colonel, USMC, volume I, prepared for the Bureau of Ordnance, Department of the Navy, Washington, D.C., 1951

The Pony Express Goes Through, Howard R. Driggs, Frederick A. Stokes, New York, copyright 1935

The Undeveloped West or Five Years in the Territory, J. H. Beadle, National Publishing Company, St. Louis, copyright 1873

"This Is Ogden" (pamphlet), Ogden Chamber of Commerce, Ogden, Utah, 1960

This Is the Place: Utah, Maurine Whipple, Alfred A. Knopf, New York, copyright 1954

Union Pacific Railroad and Other Papers, Grenville M. Dodge, 1910, U. S. Senate Documents, vol. 59, no. 447

Union Pacific Railroad, Henry Kirke White, University of Chicago Press, copyright 1895

Utah Historical Society Quarterly, vol. 22, Utah State Historical Society, copyright 1954

Who's Who in America (1926–27), A. N. Marquis Company, Chicago

Index